Farm, Ranch & Country Vacations

Farm, Ranch & Country Vacations has been published annually, or every two or three years, since 1949 by Farm & Ranch Vacations, Inc., under various titles—most recently: *Farm & Ranch Vacations; Farm, Ranch & Countryside Guide; Country Vacations U.S.A.*

Farm, Ranch & Country Vacations

by Pat Dickerman

Farm & Ranch Vacations, Inc.
36 East 57th Street, New York
Established 1949

Contents

ACKNOWLEDGMENT of outstanding help in preparing this book is due a number of contributors.

I am particularly grateful to our staff and research assistant, Connie Smith, who has again coordinated the endless sea of detail, keeping the work flowing smoothly and paving the way for a cohesive result. This is no small task with the thousands of communications, coming and going, to be routed to just the right spot, with every comma and period in its proper place.

My special thanks to Mary Perry who arrived on the scene at a propitious moment with a yen to see America and meet the people. She adjusted her travel plan to include an assignment to visit farms and ranches in 18 states on her 14,000-mile trek. What impressed her most? "The friendliness, seeing how different people live, and discovering how beautiful America is. There are so many happy families out there. It reinforces my belief in the family structure." Her reports have added many facts.

A perceptive and gifted free lance writer, John Allen, came into the picture just at the time he was needed the most. "Jet-setting at the typewriter and whizzing about the country via the alphabet" is his description of working on the copy for the listings. He also made the armchair discovery that "either the hospitality of rural America borders on the saintly, or else hundreds of vacationers take the time to sit down, haul out pen and paper, and lie."

For the much improved appearance of this edition over previous ones, I owe thanks to Karen Cure who consulted with me about a different format months ago. My thanks go also to Jay J. Smith for his cover design, and to Christina Madaio for her help in designing the fresh, new look of the pages.

My thanks extend also to the rural hosts and hundreds of their guests for the vast amount of important information which they have provided.

To all . . . my sincere appreciation.

Pat Dickerman

Introduction

A cottage by a brook in Pennsylvania...a 20,000-acre spread in Montana...a desert ranch in Arizona...a fourth generation cow outfit in Texas...a dairy farm in Wisconsin...a former private mansion in Massachusetts...a small inn in North Carolina...

So totally different, one from another. What brings them together in this travel guidebook?

Basically it's their genuine, friendly hospitality and their closeness to the land. Unstereotyped as they are, each of these ranches and farms, lodges and inns, offers in varying degree the unsophisticated enjoyment and people-to-people exchange that many vacationers seek.

WHY PEOPLE GO to these dissimilar rural spots is explained in their reports to our office—reports that deal not so much with buildings and facilities as with the quality of life, the closeness to nature and the kindness of their hosts. "Hope you'll give my hostess a four-star rating for her beautiful land, great cooking and, most important, her warm heart" is typical of guest reactions. "Absolutely nothing can take the place of all of us sitting around the large table in the kitchen—it's a grand and friendly feeling."

In the case of rural lodges and inns, it's phrases like "...relaxing...peaceful...food out of this world...hosts concerned with our enjoyment...friendly evenings in front of the fire...before we left we were anxious to return..." that run through the guests' reports.

"The house is surrounded by pasture and meadows," one of them writes, "and is adjacent to Smoky Mountain National Park where we go fishing or tubing, or take a box lunch and bike or hike past waterfalls on paths that are closed to traffic. Our hosts love the outdoors and share their knowledge of it enthusiastically.''

There's much to learn on these vacations. "It's one thing to drive by a farm and say, 'That's a cow,' writes a suburban housewife. "But it's a whole new experience to actually stay at a dairy farm, get to know the family, help in the milking process and perhaps have a chance to watch a cow give birth. There's a goodness and wholesomeness here that enriches us all.''

From a midwesterner comes the comment: "We knew the farm had really gotten to the children when Amy came downstairs soon after returning home, saw the pouring rain, and said, 'Oh no! The hay is really ruined now!' ''

Families discover that there are activities for all ages. "Our four kids range from 15 to 22 years," an educator writes, "and all of us continue to look forward to those weeks together. It is an incredibly good experience for our family. The country is magnificent, the ranch superbly operated, the crew small and the owners delightful people. The riding and fishing are great, and square dances and other activities are planned for the enjoyment of all members of the family.''

No TV, phones, newspapers or influences from the outside world also make for complete escape and relaxation at a dude ranch, as reported by an investment broker who calls it "a structured yet casual week of fun, food and fellowship.''

So many people long for the simple joys of living, like those at a camp in Maine—"awaking to the rippling of the foggy lake and going for a pre-breakfast dip with the loons and ducks, a swallow coming through the fog for a peek.''

"On an early morning ride," reports a Wyoming vacationer,

How Big Is An Acre?

We frequently toss out acreage figures in our descriptions—a 250-acre farm, for instance, or a 20,000-acre ranch. This means little to most city dwellers. Just how big *is* an acre?

Well, it is 43,560 square feet, and an average city block equals about three acres. So a 250-acre farm is like 83 city blocks—and that's a lot a hiking space.

If visualizing miles is easier, picture one square mile of land. That is 640 acres.

Now, about that 20,000-acre ranch. It is roughly the size of New York's Manhattan Island plus a good piece of the Bronx, with a population in the millions. On the ranch there's the ranch family, some cowhands and the cows. As a New Yorker wistfully remarked, "It doesn't seem fair, does it!''

"the rancher says in that reedy-deep western drawl, 'When you get to the top of that hill and the breeze hits you right in your face, aren't you just glad to be alive?' Well, there's nothing better. If you don't enjoy this ranch, you'll probably find fault with heaven."

RECOMMENDATIONS we give to the lodges, inns, ranches and farms are correlated to the varied needs of vacationers. We recommend everything from a plan-your-own-activities situation to a something-doing-all-the-time vacation. You will find listed here the simplest of family cabins—and also elegant country homes with authentic antiques and candlelight dining—and everything in between.

We describe each place for what it is. " 'Our farm is not just primitive—it's crude! You'll be walking in mud...' " reads our copy, quoting a Virginia hostess whose guests select this kind of vacation because they want to "milk the goats, ride the tractor and help mow the fields...like pioneering, with cultured and warm hosts."

We recommend with equal enthusiasm an Arizona ranch which provides a heated pool, redwood hot tub therapy room, library, Lay Kold tennis courts, Happy Hour Saloon, lots of riding and other pleasant activities and whose guests speak of the superb food, staff eager to serve, wonderful hosts and breathtaking views.

Both the Virginia farm and the Arizona ranch, with all their contrast, will meet needs of people who use this book.

To the best of our ability we have reported on each place accurately, and we hope every detail is correct. We go to great lengths to verify our facts. Detailed reports from both hosts and vacationers, one of our requirements, provide basic information, and our own firsthand visits to about 75 percent of these hosts have broadened our comprehension of what they offer their guests. In the past ten years well over 100,000 miles of travel have gone into this visiting and checking-out program. A nominal service fee paid by the hosts helps to maintain this and other special services which we provide.

The final decision on which places to include in the book is ours, and no one can buy space in it. The choice of photos from among those submitted by hosts also is ours, selected on the basis of their descriptive value, their representation of what is typical at many places and their reproductive quality.

The fact that some states are missing from our coverage is simply because we do not know of places in those areas that should be included, though undoubtedly there are many.

A place we cannot in good conscience recommend is not covered, nor is one that we feel is overcharging for what is offered. The result is a book which puts vacationers in touch with unusually good travel values.

MAKING YOUR SELECTION from the widely different places described is not difficult if you will use the details in the listings (and in the Appendix as well). People have done this for years, and many confirm the fact that things are the way we said they would be. "The description indicated everything we wanted and more than we hoped to find," wrote a guest of a Washington ranch. "We drove to the ranch immediately. That was five years ago, and we've been going there ever since."

In each description, though it is brief, we attempt to give the "feel" of what it is like to be there and what you'll find to do. In some listings details about the hosts themselves are included—their interests, cooking specialties, prior vocations and the ages of their children in case you wish to match ages with those in your family.

Whether you'll be mingling with many other guests, or whether your family alone will fill the available space, can be

---

The Appendix

To select the type of farm or ranch you want to visit, please turn to the Appendix, page 205. You also will find reference to places for young people alone or especially for adults, housekeeping accommodations, stalls or pasture if you take your horse, camping and trailer sites, smoking and drinking preferences, airstrips for private planes and hosts who speak foreign languages. It can be a helpful guide in making your choice.

---

determined by the number of guests that can be accommodated.

The services provided, and whether accommodations are somewhat luxurious or very unpretentious, are indicated to some extent by the rates.

Are you planning to travel by public transportation? If the hosts can meet you at the bus or train station or airport, that detail is given.

Will you want to do a lot of riding? Select a place that provides horses, emphasizes riding and includes it in the rates—not one that refers to "riding nearby". Expert riders might ask if there are spirited horses, fast rides, rugged all-day rides and more horses than guests (or at least plenty for riding guests).

Do . . . Don't

Visiting a working farm or ranch—an experience similar to staying with your own country cousins—is a new kind of vacation for many people. For that reason a set of guidelines may be in order.

Do be willing to fit into the farm routine rather than expecting your hosts to adjust to yours. Part of the fun is adapting to a different lifestyle.

Do go with the idea of learning a lot from a family that has a lot to teach you—if you'll let them.

Do pitch in with bed-making and some kitchen chores if your hostess has no extra help—and if she'll let you.

Do try to adapt to your hosts' house rules. They are worked out for everyone's benefit.

Do check on who supplies the linens and towels when you reserve a housekeeping cabin.

Do ask about the water supply before filling a tub or taking a long shower. In some areas water is scarce during a dry spell.

Do take along shoes that thrive on mud—and extra pairs for children who like to slosh in puddles or feed troughs or other fun places.

Do be friendly, give a little, take a little, as you'd like guests to do in your own home.

Don't take a pet along unless you first ask if it will be welcome.

Don't permit your children to go near farm machinery without the hosts' permission—and be sure they understand that riding the horses or ponies is done only with supervision.

Don't take your children to a farm if you can't control them.

Don't forget to ask about riding if that is a special interest. Are there enough horses so that you can ride every day? Are some gentle and others spirited? Or is "riding" intended for children who will love the old gray mare in the barnyard?

Don't keep the farm folks up too late. You're the ones on vacation, not they. On most working farms and ranches it's still "early to bed, early to rise . . ."

Don't be surprised if your bedroom and bath in the old farmstead are on different floors. Be grateful both are indoors.

Don't forget that farm children may be earning funds for college or a 4-H project. If they do extra work to make your visit enjoyable, a bonus will be appreciated.

Don't expect the service which you receive in a resort hotel. At a ranch or farm your relationship to the hosts is more like that of friend to friend in a private home—a special hospitality that cannot be bought.

Have you small children who want to gather eggs, feed the animals and really experience the farm they have read about in their storybooks? Choose a working farm—one that probably accommodates only a few guests at a time—and look for mention of various farm animals and crops in the copy.

A heated swimming pool, Jacuzzi or sauna, chuckwagon cookouts, breakfast rides, hayrides, overnight pack trips, sing-alongs, square dances, talent nights and the like may be among your activity preferences. Choose a guest farm or guest ranch (rather than a working ranch)—one that accommodates from fifteen to fifty, or more, guests and plans many activities for them.

Is it a holiday during off-season months—perhaps over Thanksgiving or Christmas—that you have in mind? The months in which each place is open for guests are indicated in the last line of each listing.

Also in the final line is an area location referring to a num-bered region in the state map which appears at the beginning of each state section. This gives at least an idea of what part of the state each place is in, and the exact location can be determined by the mileage and route directions from a nearby city, noted in the second paragraph.

THIRTY YEARS AGO the forerunner of this book, a 16-page brochure covering down-on-the-farm holidays in twelve eastern states, launched the first organized approach to rural hospitality.

In the years since, hundreds of thousands of our readers have milked a cow, rounded up cattle, participated in gymkhanas, poked around villages or totally relaxed at the farms, ranches, lodges and inns to which the various editions of this book have guided them.

What was considered "offbeat" in 1949 is a recognized and popular vacation pattern today, with second generation guests now turning up to milk sixth generation cows.

Gone from the listings are the "ring down" telephone numbers for rural area party lines, and the mention of "TV" as a new at-traction in the farmhouse parlor. Gone, too, are the informative but annoying symbols which this year are replaced with a longer description of each place and an everything-you-need-to-know Appendix.

In future editions there will be other improvements, many of which we expect will be sparked by your comments on the handy self-mailer at the back of this book. Tell us how you'd like to see it develop—we'll try. And tell us, too, the things you like. En-couragement never hurts to keep a good thing going!

RATES given in each listing are stated in connection with the following letter symbols:

AP: American Plan—accommodations and three meals daily

MAP: Modified American Plan—accommodations and two meals

EP: European Plan—accommodations but not meals

A: Adult   C: Child, usually 12 or under   T: Teenager

Weekly rates are generally quoted, though daily, weekly, weekend, monthly and off-season rates may be available whether or not we mention this fact. "Family rates" refer to special adjustments made for children of various ages, sometimes (but not always) applicable only if they occupy a room with their parents.

Be sure to ask hosts for specific rates not included in the listings, and it is important also to doublecheck the rates we give. To the best of our knowledge they are correct as of the date we are going to press, but in every case rates are subject to change without notice.

Rates also are subject in some areas to state and local taxes. These details should be obtained from the hosts.

BROCHURES AND RESERVATIONS involve your contacting the hosts directly by letter or telephone.

Their brochures or newsletters, which they'll be glad to forward on request, give a far more complete explanation than does our brief coverage.

Deposits generally are required to reserve space, and are returned according to each host's policy if cancellation becomes necessary.

When you contact hosts who take only a few guests at a time into their homes, it's a good idea to tell something about yourselves—the ages of your children, what you hope to do on your vacation and any specific requirements. (Cribs, for example, can be supplied by more than half of the hosts—a point to check if you will need one.) This is the time to exchange information—even snapshots—and pave the way for a congenial experience of visiting, dining and living together somewhat as an expanded family would do.

YOUNG PEOPLE receive special consideration in this book, with so many hosts who are ready to take them in along with other guests, and with a chapter especially for them about worthwhile and adventurous experiences.

What does a youngster do on a farm or ranch?

"I grew up in Houston, and I lived for the summers when I

could go to my grandparents' farm. I loved everything about it—the animals, the farm smells, the coal oil lamps at night and the fireplaces, and talking.

"I loved the moon at night and the fireflies, the coyotes howling and the cooing of the doves. I loved the deep well water and the bucket and dipper we used.

"I loved the hot days, running barefoot through the hot sand, stopping in the shade to cool my feet just enough to run, skip and jump my way over the burning ground to make it to the next shade tree. There was no way I was going to put my shoes on.

"This is the kind of atmosphere we try to give our kids. We don't watch TV; we talk instead. I was lucky enough to marry a

rancher, and I have always wanted to share our life with kids, since we enjoy it so much. When the cattle market dropped so drastically in '73, we decided to put into practice what we had been talking about, and it has worked out beautifully for us, and I think for all our friends who have stayed with us.''

Although these words are from just one of the hosts who welcomes young people (and adults, too), they speak for the warm and generous sharing that is found throughout this book.

VACATION NEEDS differ with the complexity of life in the cities and suburbs. The structured entertainment and social gatherings at a resort provide a needed change of pace and excitement for some. Motels with their impersonal and convenient housing are a boon for others.

But if it's quiet refreshment and regeneration that you need, consider the places in these pages.

For closeness to nature, wholesome activities, more or less unscheduled and carefree days, quiet and usually early-to-bed nights and sincere, friendly hosts, the vacation values offered here are hard to beat.

Perhaps one of these close-to-the-land vacations will inspire you as it did a guest at a Wyoming ranch:

''It's a land of sunburned faces and flannel shirts where the restless western winds gallop over grassy meadows, and common yellow butterflies dance the world's most graceful ballet from wildflower to wildflower, while crickets grind out a mountain melody and limber deer bound across canyons and over hillsides, happily saluting us good-bye with the flash of a white tail ... ''

Enjoy it!

P. D.

Also by Pat Dickerman:
Adventure Travel (please see page 222)

Alaska

When Alaska, America's last frontier, became the 49th state in 1959, it replaced Texas as the largest state in the Union, and Mt. McKinley became our highest peak. The Russians put their flag down on this land in 1741, and the U.S. bought it from them in 1867. "Seward's Folly" it was called, with reference to the Secretary of State's ineptness in purchasing a worthless mass of ice and snow. But the territory has turned out to be rich in marine life, wildlife, gold and other ores, lumber, oil and magnificent scenery—fjords, glaciers, snow-capped mountains and rushing rivers—a wilderness of unbelievable beauty.

BROOKS LODGE is deep in spectacular wilderness in Katmai National Monument of southwest Alaska—yet easy to reach. Wien Air Alaska schedules flights from Anchorage to King Salmon, where you connect with an amphibious bush plane for a 20-minute flight to the sand beach on Naknek Lake directly in front of the Lodge. Here you'll stay in a comfortable log cabin, and join other guests around the huge open fire and family-style dining tables where good, wholesome meals (including freshly caught salmon—a great spot for fishermen) satisfy ravenous appetites. On a guided nature hike you're apt to spot bear and see salmon jump the five-foot waterfall in their determination to journey upstream. Highlighting a visit here is a day's trek by bus and on foot (or by air) to view the stark beauty of the "Valley of Ten Thousand Smokes"—created over 65 years ago by a violent volcanic eruption.

☐ Cabins, pvt. baths, for 40 guests. For reservations or package incl. air, lodging & meals contact Wien Air Alaska. 40 air mi. E of King Salmon. *Brooks Lodge, c/o Wien Air Alaska,*

4100 International Airport Rd., Anchorage, Alaska 99502. Tel.: (907) 243-2400. Open Jun. thru Sep. 7. Area 1.

CAMP DENALI, deep in the wilderness of Mt. McKinley National Park with a panoramic view of the famous snow-capped peaks, is a "Shangri-La" for the naturalist, adventurer and photographer. "We try to acquaint each guest with the plant, bird and animal life of the sub-arctic alpine tundra world," explains conservation-minded Wally Cole, "in a region where man is only a visitor." Van trips for animal-spotting and birding or moderate to energetic hikes highlight each day, as well as delicious family-style meals. Evenings at the log lodge there are talks, slides and films which introduce and interpret the area. Chalet cabins, warmed by wood-burning stoves, are far from luxurious, but clean, comfortable and cozy—most with cold water only (showers at central bathhouse) and private privy with superb view. An outstanding Alaskan experience.

☐ Lodging for 32 guests. Weekly AP: A $560, C $420; 3 or 4 days: A $255–$342, C $191–$255. Hskpg. cabins, $35–$75/night' EP. 90 mi. W of McKinley Park Stn.; transport to/from Camp

Camp Denali, Alaska

& guided trips incl. in AP rates. *Wally & Jerri Cole, Camp Denali, P.O. Box 67, McKinley Park, Alaska 99755. Tel.: (907) 683-2290. [Winter: 683-2302.] Open Jun.–Labor Day. Area 2.*

GROSVENOR LAKE CAMP, a short bush flight from Brooks (see above) or King Salmon, was once a private summer house and now hosts one party at a time. Situated on a river between Coville and Grosvenor Lakes, it's a place for fishermen, canoeists, kayakers and nature lovers. Colors in the lakes and mountains constantly change. Everything is in motion—mergansers float by, eagles soar overhead, gulls chirp, arctic terns swim, the sky changes from rainbow to sunshine to storm in rapid succession. Catch a trout for lunch. Hike to the beaver pond. Go boating (oars or outboard). Take an extended kayak trip. Delicious meals in the cozy lodge kitchen.

☐ 2 rustic cabins for guests w./4 bunk beds in each, central bath house. Daily lodging & meals, or package incl. air. 50 air mi. NE of King Salmon. *Grosvenor Lake Camp, c/o Wien Air Alaska, 4100 International Airport Rd., Anchorage, Alaska 99502. Tel.: (907) 243-2400. Open Jun. thru Sep. 7. Area 1.*

KULIK LODGE, set in a magnificent wilderness on the shore of Nonvianuk Lake, is "a first class place I would recommend without reservation for anyone who likes to fish," advises an ardent angler. It's also for naturalists who want to observe eagles, waterfowl, peregrine falcon, hawks, a beaver dam, other wildlife and birds and hundreds of alpine flowers. Bush flights land at the Lodge's 5,000-foot runway or on the water, and wilderness flights are arranged to take you float-plane fishing, river rafting, canoeing or "flightseeing" over Katmai National Monument. The Lodge stays open in winter for x-country skiing, ice fishing and snowmobiling, and as an alternative to flying in, Bob Carroll (who has crossed Alaska by snowmobile) will meet your jet in King Salmon with snow machines and sleds for the 70-mile winter-wonderland trip to the lodge. Big open fires and excellent meals in the log lodge.

☐ 8 cabins ea. for 2-4 guests, w./elec., heat, pvt. baths, $100–$200/day/person incl. some bush flights, guides, etc. 60 air mi. NE of King Salmon. *Bob Carroll, Kulik Lodge, c/o Wien Air Alaska, 4100 International Airport Rd., Anchorage, Alaska 99502. Tel.: (907) 243-2400. Open all year. Area 1.*

Arizona

Arizona is a blend of the West, Old Mexico and the Indian. It became the 48th state in 1912, having been a territory since the Mexican flag last flew there in 1853. Before the Mexicans, the Spanish claimed it, and before that the Indians were there for perhaps 25,000 years. Today it is a land of cowboys and rodeos, ghost towns, prehistoric pueblos, red rock canyons, abandoned forts, legendary mines, tribal fairs, picturesque desert, rugged mountains, lakes and streams, cow towns, lumber towns and sprawling tourist boom towns. Everywhere the turbulent Old West rubs elbows with the New—a fascinating colorful past still there to be seen.

KAY EL BAR GUEST RANCH, one of Arizona's first, nestles in a small valley along the banks of the Hassayampa River. Its authentic adobe buildings in the Spanish hacienda style have put it on the National Register of Historic Places. The hospitable Petersens (sons 9 and 14) provide family-style meals with homemade bread and pies, and take guests on breakfast rides and cookouts. There's riding and swimming at the ranch. Golf is nearby, as are Wickenburg's rodeos and square dances. "The clear morning air was superb; I could have run forever," a jogger-guest reports. "Excellent food, top staff, an unforgettable sunrise ride, a friendly place to visit," comment other guests.

☐ Rooms & suites, pvt. baths, for 30 guests. Daily AP: $70–$100 dbl., $45–$60 sgl. Also 2 hskpg. units: $125–$150 weekly EP. 54 mi. W of Phoenix. From Wickenburg, go 3 mi. E on Rincon Rd. Meet plane in Phoenix, $35/trip; plane/train/bus in Wickenburg, no chg. *Chuck & Carol*

Price Canyon Ranch, Arizona

Petersen, Kay El Bar Guest Ranch, P.O. Box 2419, Wickenburg, Arizona 85358. Tel.: (602) 684-7593. Open Oct.-May. Area 3.

LOBA LODGE, surrounded by the tall Ponderosa pines of Prescott National Forest, offers a lot of tranquility and relaxation in a setting of natural beauty. "The lodge is well operated with very comfortable cottages (carpeted, heated throughout, good bedding, well-equipped kitchens, fireplaces and wood) and a friendly atmosphere," describes a guest who has conducted several painting workshops here. It is well suited for small seminars and workshop groups, and for nature lovers, birders, hikers, fishing (Goldwater Lake), antiquing, horse races, and exploring Prescott (20,000 population). You also can make easy day trips to the Grand Canyon, Jerome (ghost town), Oak Creek Canyon, Indian ruins and Hopi and Navajo Reservations.

◻ 13 hskpg. units accom. 35 guests. EP: $25–$37/unit daily for 2 persons, $5 ea. addl.; weekly $159–$235 for 2. 100 mi. N. of Phoenix, 80 mi. SW of Flagstaff. From Prescott, go S on Senator Hwy. 4½ mi. *Virginia Jensen, Loba Lodge, Senator Hwy., Prescott, Arizona 86301. Tel.: (602) 445-1987. Open all year. Area 3.*

LOMAQACI is an 8-acre resort on famous Oak Creek. From a Hopi word, its name means "place of happiness." Bird watchers, artists, film crews and just plain vacationers come from far and near to experience Oak Creek Canyon's quiet beauty. "The accommodations are excellent and clean," guests say. "It is beautifully managed and maintained, and Mrs. Walker is a fine hostess. It's good to get back to the simpler joys of life." From Lomaqaci you can tour historic northern Arizona—the Grand Canyon, Flagstaff, Walnut Canyon cliff dwellings, Montezuma's Castle, Tuzigoot (a pueblo village of the 12th century) and Jerome (a ghost town). Lomaqaci's jewel-like setting is half a mile from the center of Sedona, "art capitol of the West." Playground for children.

☐ Air-cond. cottages (15) w./pvt. baths; most have living room, bedrooms, kitchen. Daily EP: $25–$40 for 2, $5 ea. addl. 7th day free. 110 mi. N of Phoenix, 27 mi. S of Flagstaff, on US 89 Alt. Meet bus in Sedona, no chg. *Mrs. Nora R. Walker, Lomaqaci, Box 46, Sedona, Arizona 86336. Tel.: (602) 282-7912. Open Mar.–Dec. Area 1.*

PRICE CANYON RANCH, a hard-working cattle ranch, covers 23,000 acres just 40 miles from the Mexican border. It stretches from rolling grassland at 4,400 feet to high mountain meadows and pine forest at 9,000 feet. "You feel as though you are visiting with family," reports a guest, "gaining insight into a way of life." You may learn to ride a horse, rope a calf, round up the cows and help with the branding—or just be an observer. Pack trips (extra), fishing and good food are part of the scene, plus the warmth and hospitality of the Andersons. Guests call it a "beautiful, breathtaking setting, magnificent for nature lovers."

☐ Accom. 3 families or 25 dorm-style guests in sgl. or dbl. room and bunkhouses, pvt. baths. Weekly AP: A $210–$245, T $88–$140, C $70, incl. riding. Also daily rates. Trailer sites, $4/day. Pack trip, $50/day. 160 mi. SE of Tucson. From Douglas go 40 mi. NE on US 80 to Apache, follow signs to ranch. Meet plane/bus in Tucson, $65/carload; in Douglas, no chg. *Scotty & Alice Anderson, Price Canyon Ranch, P.O. Box 1065, Douglas, Arizona 85607. Tel.: (602) 558-2383. Open all year. Area 4. (See chapter, "For Teens and Under.")*

RANCHO DE LA OSA, an old Spanish land grant along the Mexican border, is considered the only authentic hacienda-style ranch in the traditional quadrangle pattern remaining in the

Southwest. Some of the buildings are over 200 years old. There's riding over miles of grassland or in the mountains, with just the right mount for each guest from among 100 head raised on the ranch. For bird watchers—both regional and Mexican birds. You can join in ranch activities, drive to the village across the border, or stay close to the heated pool. "Wonderful hosts and marvelous meals," comments a guest. It's an area steeped in history, once the scene of a border dispute. The Papago Indian Reservation adjoins the property.

☐ Cottages & rooms w./pvt. baths & fireplaces accom. 42 guests. Daily AP: A $44–$50, C $28, incl. riding. 60 mi. SW of Tucson—go 22 mi. W on Rt. 86 to 3 points, 47 mi. S. on Rt. 286. Meet plane/train/bus in Tucson, $40/carload. *Al & Doris Anderson, Rancho de la Osa, Sasabe, Arizona 85633. Tel.: (602) 823-4321. Open all year. Area 4.*

SUNGLOW MISSION RANCH is in a secluded Chiricahua Mountain valley at 5,200 feet and near the Mexican border. "It is ideal for complete relaxation," explain the hosts, "and offers luxurious housekeeping casas around a lovely adobe Chapel for meditation and worship of all faiths, providing that quiet atmosphere so necessary for spiritual regeneration." Recreation includes horseback riding, hiking, birding, rock hunting and fishing in Sunglow Lake. Stereo recordings and the best in secular and religious literature are provided in the library. Nearby historic points of interest include Bonita Canyon, Chiricahua National Monument, Fort Bowie, Cochise Stronghold, Tombstone, Bisbee, and Douglas and Aqua Prieta on the border.

☐ Accom. 16 guests in 7 fully equipped casas, all w./pvt. bath. Weekly EP: $135 for 1 person, $165–$195 for 2, $225–$310 for 3 or 4. Also weekend & multiple-week rates. 50 mi. N of Douglas, 48 mi. S of Wilcox—42 mi. S on Rt. 186, 5 mi. E on Turkey Creek Rd., right for 1 mi. Meet plane in Tucson, $40/carload. *Wood & Bette Perrett, Jeanne & Al Shaffer, Sunglow Mission Ranch, Pearce, Arizona 85625. Tel.: (602) 824-3364. Open all year. Area 4.*

WHITE STALLION RANCH, on 4,000 acres at the foot of the Tucson Mountains in a 100,000-acre game preserve, has plenty of wide-open space. "Horseback riding here is terrific," stress the Trues. There's also hiking, birding, rock hunting, a heated pool and redwood hot tub therapy room, and large library. "We love this place," exclaims a guest, "the hosts are wonderful, food superb, entire staff eager to serve. Breathtaking views, and congenial guests.'' You'll like the hayrides, movies, shuffleboard, croquet, ping-pong, pool table, putting green, bridge, chess, Lay Kold tennis courts and the Happy Hour Saloon. The Trues raise quarter horses and Belgians, Longhorn steers and exotic birds. The cowboys rodeo in the ranch arena. Two sons, 19 and 14, help out. Barbecues, cookouts, Indian oven dinners. Things are friendly—count on knowing everyone within hours, even if you come alone.

☐ Accom. 65 guests in suites, dbl. & sgl. rooms, all pvt. baths. Daily AP: $44–$60, C $34–$36. Riding incl. 14 mi. NW of Tucson—take I-10 to Cortaro exit, W to Silverbell Rd., right & follow signs. Meet plane/train/bus in Tucson, no chg. *Allen & Cynthia True, White Stallion Ranch, Rt. 9, Box F-567, Tucson, Arizona 85704. Tel.: (602) 297-0252. Open Oct. thru 1st wk. May. Area 4.*

White Stallion Ranch, Arizona

Arkansas

Take a measure of southern charm and some folksiness from the prairie states, mix well, and you have the recipe for an Arkansas welcome. Originally part of the Louisiana Purchase, the area won statehood in 1836 and soon became a starting point for far west expeditions and covered wagon caravans headed for California and gold. Folk tales flourish here, with subjects ranging from the razorback to the "Arkansas Traveler." In the Ozark Mountains you may meet up with a real hillbilly or the fabricated variety found in Dogpatch, U.S.A., where Al Capp's characters entertain tourists.

ROLLING ACRES RANCH rolls across 240 beautiful Ozark acres. Here Lindsey and Loreva and their children (21 and 14) raise ducks, lambs and beef cattle (primarily Charolais). They hike to mountaintops, go fishing, and take in local craft shows, folk musicals and square dances. Produce from the farm turns up in good southern cooking. "I'm impressed with the house, hosts and scenery," says a visitor who gives Rolling Acres top marks. The Ozark Folk Center and Blanchard Caverns are close by. Non-drinkers and non-smokers preferred.

☐ 2 family-sized rooms w./shared bath for 8 guests. Weekly MAP: A $140, C $100, babies free. Also newly refurbished home in secluded area of farm; inquire re EP rates. 125 mi. N of Little Rock. From court square in Mountain View take Hwy. 66 3 mi. toward Leslie. *Lindsey & Loreva Harness, Rolling Acres Ranch, Newnata Rt., Mountain View, Arkansas 72560. Tel.: (501) 269-8545. Open Apr.–Oct. Area 2.*

SCOTT VALLEY DUDE RANCH in the Ozarks features western atmosphere plus full southern hospitality with "extra

Scott Valley Dude Ranch, Arkansas

good food and all you want of it," as one satisfied guest writes. Plenty of riding, a heated pool, tennis (with night lights), and fishing—rainbow trout in the White River, bass and crappie in Lake Norfork. Guides and full equipment make fishing trips a success. Within driving range are the Ozark Folk Center, Dogpatch U.S.A., Silver Dollar City, Blanchard Spring Caverns, Top O' the Ozark Tower, and the largest rainbow trout hatchery in the nation. For children—a playground, pony cart rides, cookouts and hayrides. Daughter Kathy is an experienced wrangler, lifeguard, and hostess for teenagers.

   ☐ 28 air-cond. units (pvt. baths, maid service) accom. 100 guests. Weekly AP: A $180, C $135 (to 8 yrs., $90). Riding incl. 150 mi. N of Little Rock—go N on US 65 to US 62, E to Mountain Home, 4½ mi. S on Rt. 5, follow signs 3 mi. Meet plane/bus in Mountain Home, no chg.; plane in Harrison, $25. *Gene & Mary Scott, Scott Valley Dude Ranch, RVG 2, Mountain Home, Arkansas 72653. Tel.: (501) 425-5136. Open Mar.–Nov. Area 1.*

California

In 1848 a grizzled prospector shouted (so we're told), "Eureka! I have found it." His words exploded into the Gold Rush of '49 and launched California into statehood (1850) and an influx of settlers that still has not ceased. Today it is the nation's most populous state. Explorers first came to California in the 1500s— among them, Sir Francis Drake. Spanish colonization, the Franciscan missions, Mexican rule and independence followed in rapid succession. The state's many national parks, monuments, forests and wilderness areas might well cause "Eureka!" to be shouted today by the naturalist, to whom scenic beauty, not gold, symbolizes true wealth.

CAMANCHE NORTH SHORE RESORT in the Mother Lode Country overlooks Lake Camanche—ten miles long and three across. You'll sail, fish, waterski, play tennis or go houseboating, cycling or canoeing; and you can hike or ride horseback on the resort's 1,000 wooded acres. Hunting, trap and skeet shooting if you wish, or float trips on the Mokelumne River, hayrides, pony rides and gold panning. The resort's facilities are very complete—coffee shop, restaurant/bar, stables, rodeo arena—all that's needed for a full vacation or for conferences and seminars.

☐ 10 motel rooms & 20 housekeeping cottages, pvt. baths, accom. 100 guests. Daily EP: Dbl. rooms, $24; hskpg. cottages for 4–6, $48–$72; rollaways $6. Also weekly rates. 20% disct. Nov. thru Feb. 50 mi. SE of Sacramento; 40 mi. NE of Stockton—go E on US 88 thru Clements, left 3 mi. to Liberty Rd., right 8 mi. Meet plane/bus in Stockton or Lodi, $5/person. *Dick & Neva Kelsey, Camanche North Shore Resort, R.R. 1,*

Ione, California 95640. Tel.: (209) 763-5121. Open all year. Area 4.

CHOLAME CREEK RANCH. Cattle, horses and hay are raised at this 5,000-acre family ranch named after the picturesque creek, lined with cottonwood and willows, which flows through it. "We love to entertain people," write the congenial Van Horns, "whether they want to be cared for royally or just enjoy the peace and tranquility and be alone." They prefer having only a few guests at a time, or a club group where all have similar interests. (They save June through August for young people only—see Chapter "For Teens and Under.") Activities include riding lessons, trail rides, brandings, campouts, swimming in the new pool and hunting fossils and rocks. Barbecues and hot biscuits ("everything from scratch") are specialties.

    □ 3 dbls. in ranch house, 4 bunkhouses, pvt. & shared baths. Daily AP: A $36–$49, C $30–$32, 10% less Jan.–Apr.; riding extra. 200 mi. N of Los Angeles. From Paso Robles, go 31 mi. E on Hwy. 46, 14 mi. N at Parkfield exit. Meet plane/train in San Luis Obispo, $20/carload; bus in Paso Robles, $10/carload. *Martin & Gloria Van Horn, Cholame Creek Ranch, P.O. Box 8-R, Cholame, California 93431. Tel.: (805) 463-2320. Open all year. Area 5.*

CIRCLE BAR B GUEST RANCH—1,000 acres in the Santa Ynez Mountains only 3½ miles from ocean beaches—combines ranching and dinner theater. Fine horses carry you along trails with breathtaking views of mountains and sea by day. In the evening, barbecues and then comedy in a little red barn playhouse with ranch guests and local folk mingling at the latter. "A wonderful ranch for families," writes a guest, "with charming, relaxed rustic atmosphere and congenial hostess." Heated pool and sun-dappled patio, rodeos, square dances, fishing and fireside coziness add to the old-fashioned fun.

    □ 12 (somewhat rustic) rooms in house & cabins accom. 30 guests. Daily MAP: A $30–$35, C $2 per yr. of age up to 10 yrs. Riding extra. 125 mi. NW of Los Angeles. From Santa Barbara—go 22 mi. N on US 101, 3½ mi. up Refugio Canyon. Meet plane/train/bus in Santa Barbara, no chg. *Mrs. Florence Brown, Circle Bar B Guest Ranch, Rt. 1, Box 258, Goleta, California 93017. Tel.: (805) 968-1113. Open all year. Area 5.*

COFFEE CREEK RANCH, surrounded by high peaks of the Trinity Alps, was taken over several years ago by the Hartmans (children 6 and 9) to help families "get away from the rat race and totally relax." This they do in old, renovated cabins among the trees and along a stream. They swim in the heated pool or creek, go fishing and canoeing, pan for gold and ride the 30 horses which the Hartmans raise. Kiddie Korral and playground for youngsters, trapshoot and rifle range for grown-ups. Good home cooking—Thanksgiving dinner once a week! Beginning this winter: x-country skiing, sleds, inner tubes, saucers, ice skating and sleigh rides.

☐ Accom. 50 guests in 2 sgls., 14 cabins, pvt. baths. Weekly AP: A $199–$219, T $179–$199, C $100–$110. Disct. before May 26 & after Sep. 7. Under 2 yrs., no chg., cribs avail. Winter rates. 72 mi. NW of Redding; 45 mi. N of Weaverville—N on Hwy. 3 to Coffee Creek Rd., left 4½ mi. Meet plane/bus in Redding, $25/carload. *Mark & Ruth Hartman, Coffee Creek Ranch, Dept. FG, P.O., Trinity Center, California 96091. Tel.: (916) 266-3343, ask for Ruth. Open May–Oct., Dec.–Mar. Area 1.*

Circle Bar B Guest Ranch, California

FLYING H RANCH means horses, horses, horses—plus all the things that go with them: a 300- by 150-foot arena, trail rides, overnight pack trips, breakfast cookouts, amateur rodeos, chuckwagon dinners and horse shows. The ranch breeds and raises Belgian draft horses and Black Angus cattle. Lots more to do—tennis, swimming, sauna and hot tub, cycling, hiking and shuffleboard. Fishing, boating, and waterskiing on nearby Lake Nacimiento. Pony cart driving and hayrides. Kiddies get their own play area and petting zoo. Delicious western family-style meals are featured, with ranch hands joining in on campfire sings. Built just five years ago, the ranch offers pleasant accommodations and open space for all ages.

□ 50 cabins (most air-cond.) & pvt. baths accom. 100 guests. Weekly AP, Apr.–Nov.: A $198, C $139 (1–3 yrs., $77). Daily AP: A $35, C $21.50 (1–3 yrs., $12). Riding, $6/hr. Weekend, off-season, sr. citizen & group rates. 214 mi. N of Los Angeles, 244 mi. S of San Francisco. 13 mi. NW of Paso Robles—follow L. Nacimiento & G-14 signs. Meet plane in Paso Robles, $3, or bus, $2/person. Meet train in San Luis Obispo, $7.50/person. *Gordon & Arline Heath, Flying H Ranch, P.O. Box 95-A, Paso Robles, California 93446. Tel.: (805) 238-5534. Open all year. Area 5.*

HUNEWILL CIRCLE H GUEST RANCH, a 5,000-acre spread, has been in the family since 1861, perched on the slopes of Yosemite peaks. The old white-frame ranch house opened to guests in 1931. It's a real ranch in cattle country, with 2,000 head of cattle and wranglers who know every turn of the trails. People who prefer simplicity and informality turn up here year after year. You'll join in steak fries, square dancing, hiking, trail rides, swimming, many ranch activities and family-style meals with all the good wholesome food you can eat—most of it rasied on the ranch. "Really great," reports a guest, "looks just like an old ranch should look."

□ 45 guests accom. in ranch house rooms & cottages, pvt. baths. Rates changing somewhat; please request. Off-season & group rates. Under 10 yrs., 50% disct. Baby-sitting provided. 91 mi. N of Bishop. From So. California take US 395 N to ranch. Meet bus in Bridgeport, no chg. *Mrs. LeNore M. Hunewill, Hunewill Circle H Guest Ranch, Box 368, Bridgeport, California 93517. Tel.: (714) 932-7710. [Winter tel.: (702) 465-2201 or 2325.] Open May 15–Sep. 20. Area 4.*

LOR-O RANCH. Peacocks on a ranch? Lor-O raises them along with Black Angus cattle, milk cows, chickens, hay, horses,

Lor-O Ranch, California

ducks and dogs. Trout in the pond, too. Klamath National
Forest and Salmon Trinity Alps Wilderness Area surround the
rolling meadows and pastures, complete with a ghost town and
old mines. The ranch features good cooking, a small bar, spectacular views, fishing, bird watching, riding, swimming and
panning for gold. Overnight pack trips to an upper lake for
weekly guests. Hosts' teenagers are guides and help with chores.
   ☐ Accom. 23 in 3 cottages, pvt. baths, & 2 cabins with
separate bathhouse. Weekly AP: A $260-$360, C 50% less;
disct. May & Oct. Rates incl. horses, open bar, overnight pack
trip. 120 mi. NW of Redding—take I-5 thru Weed, Gazelle-
Edgewood exit to Gazelle, left to Callahan, left to East Fork
Campground, left 6 mi. up the South Fork. Meet plane in
Medford, $10/carload, or in Ft. Jones, $5; meet bus in Yreka,
$5/carload. *Dick & Ethelyn Barrett, Bill & Patsy Marcy, Lor-O
Ranch, Star Rt. Box 915, Cecilville, California 96018. Tel.:
(916) Sawyers Bar Toll Stn. 4681. [Winter tel.: (213) 353-0536.]
Open May thru Oct. Area 1.*

M BAR J GUEST RANCH near Sequoia National Park features
riding—and Bunny's cooking with locally grown fresh
vegetables, fruits and meats. Guests (who come from as far
away as Germany and Japan) also enjoy hiking by the stream,
splashing in the pool, square dancing on the patio, using the

library, orienteering, or just doing nothing at all. And they enjoy Archie's trail parties into Sequoia for a hamburger and chili cookout. It's a happy life with good riding in a quiet, oak-studded valley. Cross-country skiing in the parks until May.

☐ Accom. 26 guests in 8 cabins & 2-bedroom mobile home, pvt. baths. Weekly AP: A $230–$240, C $144 (4–7 yrs., $108), riding incl. Also daily rates. 216 mi. N of Los Angeles. 35 mi. E of Visalia—go 17 mi. E on Hwy. 198, ½ mi. N on Hwy. 216, right on J-21 (Dry Creek Rd.) for 18 mi. Meet plane/bus in Visalia, no chg. *Archie & Bunny Stockebrand, M Bar J Guest Ranch, Box 121-G, Badger, California 93603. Tel.: (209) 337-2513. Open Mar.–Sep. Area 3.*

QUARTER CIRCLE U RANKIN RANCH, a historic 31,000-acre working spread, offers a lodge, cabins, gardens and pool tastefully developed for guests. Since 1863 the ranch has been

Quarter Circle U Rankin Ranch, California

M Bar J Guest Ranch, California

part of California's exciting history—as an Indian encampment, a stagecoach stop, and once visited by the infamous Spanish bandit Joaquin Murietta. "We're the real thing and you'll be welcome," the Rankins say. Besides cattle drives, trail rides, cookouts and hayrides, you'll find fishing, tennis, swimming, dancing and games—and special rides for children. Also patio parties. A place to relax and enjoy yourself, as one family puts it.

☐ 12 air-cond. rooms in cabins, pvt. baths, for 38 guests. Weekly AP: A $280–$350, C $215–$255, incl. riding; also daily & off-season rates. 125 mi. NE of Los Angeles; 42 mi. E of Bakersfield—go N on I-5 to Arvin cutoff, thru town, E 1½ mi. on Hwy. 58, left on Caliente cutoff to 3 mi. past town, left at fork, Caliente-Bodfish Rd. 10 mi. to ranch. Meet plane/train/bus in Bakersfield, no chg. for weekly guests. *The Rankin Family, Quarter Circle U Rankin Ranch, Box 36-A, Caliente, California 93518. Tel.: (802) 867-2511. Open Apr.–Nov. Area 5.*

ROCKING R RANCH. Hosts Bob and Dottie Butcher describe their 1,000-acre guest ranch as "truly a family vacation area," with activities for all ages. Parents can join in with their children, or have time alone. Rocking R is in a secluded mountain valley with magnificent views. You can ride, fish, swim, or bird watch (it's a wildlife haven). "Excellent hospitality," report the guests, "and hosts who are willing to 'custom-tailor' things." Evenings begin with good farm meals, and campfires often follow.

☐ 5 well-equipped A-frame cabins w./bath, kitchen & fireplace, & ranch house rooms. Accom. 30 guests. Weekly EP: A $130, C $120. Weekly AP: A $195, C $170. Riding incl. 300 mi. N of San Francisco. 18 mi. SW of Yreka—go S on I-5 to Rt. 3, 9 mi. W to Moffett Creek Rd., 7 mi. S & 3 mi. W to ranch. Meet bus in Yreka, no chg.; plane in Medford, $15. *Bob & Dottie Butcher, Rocking R Ranch, Moffett Creek Rd., Fort Jones, California 96032. Tel.: (916) 468-2393. Open May–Oct. Area 1.*

Colorado

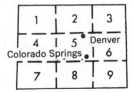

In Colorado, which has been a state since 1876, be prepared for spectacular mountain scenes. Solid rock cliffs rise perpendicularly into lofty jagged peaks—an awesome spine of rock that forms the Continental Divide. Unforgettable are the knarled old trees at timberline, lush green valleys thousands of feet below, swift streams, and the mix of golden aspen and dark evergreens in autumn. Back in the sheltered canyons sit the old-time ranches which today have changed their specialty from raising cattle to entertaining guests, though some do both. You'll find ghost towns here, and old mines, fascinating museums and relics of the Old West.

ARAPAHO VALLEY RANCH is deftly described by one guest as "a place to rough it without having it too rough!" There's fun for the whole family—breakfast rides, backpack trips, hayrides, fishing, boating, square dancing. Swimming in a heated pool. Movies and songfests, too, with supervision for the children. It's a homey, rustic resort "where roads end and the trails begin," as Bob and Carol describe it. The fabulously beautiful setting makes it an artist's paradise, and the family-style meals appeal to all.

□ Accom. 75 guests in 19 cabins w./pvt. baths, most w./fireplaces. Weekly AP: A $185, C $115. MAP: A $170, C $100. EP: $237 for 2, $21 ea. addl. Riding extra. From Granby on US 40, go 6 mi. N on US 34 & Rt. 6. Meet plane/train/bus in Granby, no chg. *Bob & Carol Wild, Arapaho Valley Ranch, Box 142-V, Granby, Colorado 80446. Tel.: (303) 887-3495. Open Jun.–Sep. Area 2.*

Arapaho Valley Ranch, Colorado

CANYON RANCH, deep in Dry Creek Canyon where the Ute Indians once lived, is a real working ranch. Guests participate in riding, cattle drives and cookouts, explore ghost towns and hunt for Indian artifacts. They swim in the creek, go on adventurous jeep trips and become deer watchers—sometimes spotting as many as 50 in one day. Ranch-style meals are tasty and mostly home-grown. "We enjoy sharing our beautiful country and way of life," writes Bea. One poetically-inclined guest thanked them for "dreams that will last for the rest of my life." Reports another, "Our kids haven't stopped talking about the ranch."

 □ Accom. 12 guest in 2 cabins, w./pvt. baths, & bunkhouse for 8 w./shower house. Weekly AP: A $140, C $90, riding incl. 13 mi. S of Delta—go S to Coors Granary, right 11 mi., sharp left, right on 1st gravel rd., follow signs. Meet bus/plane in Montrose or Olathe, no chg. *Bob & Bea Frisch, Canyon Ranch, Rt. 1, Box 61A, Olathe, Colorado 81425. Tel.: (303) 323-5288. Open all year. Area 4.*

BEAVERS GUEST RANCH is high in the Rockies, just west of the Great Divide and bordered on three sides by the Arapaho National Forest. With a string of 150 horses the big thing here is riding—"one of the best riding programs in the state," the Catlows maintain. "Our rides are split—slow, medium and fast—according to riding ability." There's the right mount for each rider, instruction in the ring and rides twice a day. The good news at mealtime is provided by Clarence and Lois LaPhan, chefs here for 17 years and famous through the region for their homemade breads, pastries and desserts, and a beautiful Tuesday evening buffet. Non-riders go on daily auto trips through the historic area—including the top of Corona Pass and Rocky Mountain National Park. There's a heated pool, a lake for boating, and a special counselor program for children.

 □ Accom. 150 guests in sgl., dbl. & family-sized rooms, all pvt. baths. Weekly MAP: A $270-$370, C $243-$306, incl. riding. 10% less 1st 3 wks. Jun. & 1st 2 wks. Sep. 70 mi W of Denver—W on I-70 for 40 mi., right on US 40 for 30 mi. Meet plane/train/bus in Denver, $8.50/person. *Wright & Jan Catlow, Beavers Guests Ranch, Box 43, Winter Park, Colorado 80482. Tel.: (303) 726-5741. Open Jun.-mid-Sep. Area 2.*

COLORADO TRAILS RANCH, 515 acres in the mountains, has top horses, scenic trails and activities for everyone. Riding lessons for beginners through advanced; also instruction in trapshooting, riflery, archery, swimming, water skiing and other sports. Heated pool, whirlpool spa and professional tennis courts. "Colorado Trails allowed our family a structured week of fun, food, and fellowship," reports a guest. "Everyone enjoys our 'nightlife' too," adds host Dick Elder—"square dancing, staff shows, melodramas, powwows around the fire, hayrides, steak fries and more." Other specialities: all-day and overnight pack trips, breakfast rides, trout fishing. Children's program offers "things kids like most."

☐ Accom. 80 guests in modern cabins w./pvt. baths, wall-to-wall carpeting, electric heat. No bar. Weekly AP: A $245–$325, C $195–$275, riding incl. 310 mi. SW of Denver, 12 mi. NE of Durango on Florida Rd. Meet plane/bus in Durango, no chg. *The Elders, Colorado Trails Ranch, Box 848, Durango, Colorado 81301. Tel.: (303) 247-5055. Open Jun.–Sep. Area 7.*

COULTER GUEST RANCH is a place where you "really get away and relax." You can ride, swim, fish at this 1,000-acre old-time ranch in evergreen mountains. Quarter horses and pets, and family-style meals featuring "homemade everything." Guests return for the "completely rustic, intimate and so 'un-fancy' " life, for the fun of trail rides, cookouts and jeep trips, and for the chance to just sit back and relax.

☐ 8 cabins w./pvt. baths & fireplaces for 30 guests. Weekly AP: A $225–$242, C $112–$202, incl. riding. 220 mi. W of Denver, 21 mi. NE of Rifle. Meet train/bus in Rifle, no chg., plane in Grand Junction, $20/carload. *Buddy & Sandy Luby, Coulter Guest Ranch, Box 906-F, Rifle, Colorado 81650. Tel.: (303) 625-1473. Open May–Sep. Area 4.*

DON K RANCH covers 2,000 historic acres surrounded by the San Isabel National Forest with spectacular high mountain riding trails. The huge log lodge, pine-panelled cottages, stone fireplaces, barns, corrals and luxurious pool present a picture of western hospitality—as do the trailwise horses, one to call your own during your stay. Easy rides and instruction for beginners, challenging rides for the experienced. Three generations of Koenigs oversee a program ranging from breakfast rides and steak barbecues to square dancing, songfests, marshmallow roasts, old-time movies and meals that have guests raving about fresh-baked bread and pastries. Ranch rodeos every Friday. Teen activities and full-time children's counselors.

☐ Main lodge & cottages accom. 65 guests; all but 6 rooms have pvt. baths. Weekly AP: A $260–$290, C 20% disct. 70 mi. SW of Colorado Springs; 30 mi. W of Pueblo—take Hwy. 96 W

Drowsy Water Ranch, Colorado

22 mi., left on Don K Ranch Rd. 5 mi., thru ranch gate 2½ mi. Meet plane/bus in Pueblo, $10/family. *The Koenigs, Don K Ranch, 2677 S. Siloam Rd., Pueblo, Colorado 81005. Tel.: (303) 784-6600. Open May 15–Sep. 15. Area 8.*

DOUBLE JK RANCH, at 9,000 feet elevation next to Rocky Mountain National Park, was homesteaded in 1907. There's lots to do at this guest ranch, though nothing is regimented. Horseback riding, jeep trips, hayrides and cookouts are frequent activities. For swimming, a new pool and spa; for games, a new recreation building; and a lodge for conversation, cards, reading or dozing by the fire. Once-a-week square dancing, marshmallow roasts, steak fries and "mellerdramas." Non-smokers and non-drinkers preferred. "Nothing beats the friendliness and home-cooking," says a guest.

☐ 15 rustic, carpeted cabins,. pvt. baths, for 59 guests. Weekly AP: A $195, C $170; riding extra. 67 mi. NW of Denver—go N on I-25, W on US 36 thru Boulder & N to Lyons, 24 mi. W on Rt. 7. Meet bus in Estes Park, no chg. *Joel & Jean Ann Kleeves, Double JK Ranch, Box F, Longs Peak Rt., Estes Park, Colorado 80517. Tel.: (303) 586-3537. Open Jun.–Aug. Area 2.*

DROWSY WATER RANCH, in a mountain valley bordering national forest land at an elevation of 8,500 feet makes a specialty of family vacations. "The people at the ranch bend over backwards to make everyone feel at home and have a good time," writes a guest. With over 75 horses, they match each rider with just the right horse and provide instruction, breakfast rides, all-day rides, pack trips and gymkhana rodeos. Also jeep trips, a heated pool, square dancing, movies and carnivals. Nearby golf and tennis. Family-style meals and good fishing—"you catch 'em, and we'll cook 'em," say the Foshas.

☐ Cabins & lodges w./pvt. baths accom. 56 guests. Weekly AP: A $260–$300, incl. riding. Also family & daily rates. 97 mi. W of Denver. From Granby, go 7 mi. W on US 40. Meet plane/bus in Granby, no chg. *Ken & Randy-Sue Fosha, Drowsy Water Ranch, Box 147-F, Granby, Colorado 80446. Tel.: (303) 725-3456. Open Jun.–Sep. Area 2.*

INDIAN HEAD GUEST RANCH is managed by Frank McGraw, who was born here, and his wife, Ruth. Comfortable old cabins along a bubbling stream are at the end of the road in a secluded yet accessible valley surrounded by high mountains, meadows and alpine tundra. Nostalgia and friendliness seem to permeate the atmosphere—"like going home." Miles of trails for horseback riding wind into Rocky Mountain National Park and Roosevelt National Forest. "Our alpine ride is for the memory book," Frank promises. And you'll remember fishing, hiking, breakfast rides, the heated pool, songfests and cookouts— "every meal has a specialty." A fine place for families. Golf and tennis nearby.

☐ Accom. 40 guests in comfortable, non-luxurious cabins, pvt. baths. Weekly AP: A $245, C $120–$200, incl. riding. Also daily rates. 62 mi. NW of Denver, 6½ mi. NE of Estes Park. Meet bus in Estes Park, no chg. *Frank & Ruth McGraw, Indian Head Guest Ranch, Box 2260, Estes Park, Colorado 80517. Tel.: (303) 586-5291. [Winter: Write Box 990, or call (303) 586-5412.] Open end-May to mid-Sep. Area 2.*

LAKE MANCOS RANCH, at 8,000 feet adjoining the San Juan National Forest, is big on riding, with over 65 horses and five wranglers who guide trail riders on different trails each day. "We start easy and end with all-day rides and a campout," Lloyd explains. Non-riders gravitate to the heated swimming pool or Jacuzzi, go on hikes and jeep rides, or pull themselves away to visit Mesa Verde National Park or ride the narrow gauge railway from Durango to Silverton. A flexible program for kids, one for teens that bends to fit their interests, and a weekly rodeo in the ranch arena on Saturday. For 23 years guests have been coming here for the "casual and relaxing family atmosphere, excellent fishing and riding, outstanding food, and privacy from the outside world."

□ Accom. 60 guests in sgls. & dbls. w./pvt. baths in ranch house, and 13 cabins w./2 or 3 bedrooms, 2 baths, living room, porch. Weekly AP: A $240, C $168–$192, riding extra. Early Jun. & Sep. 10% less. 35 mi. W of Durango—W on US 160 to Mancos, N on Rd. 184 for .3 mi., right on black top for 5 mi. Meet plane or bus, Cortez or Durango. *Lloyd & Kathy Sehnert, Lake Mancos Ranch, Box 218-F, Mancos, Colorado 81328. Tel.: (303) 533-7900. Open Jun.–Sep. Area 7.*

LAZY H RANCH, at 8,300 feet with a view up Rock Creek Valley, is a place for "good food, good horses, good accomodations, good family fun and relaxation," writes host Bill Halligan. "We have big, hearty, filling, homemade, natural, delicious meals. Diet before you come!" Besides lots of riding and a weekly gymkhana there are hiking trails, cookouts, a heated pool and children's program, and historic places like Central City within easy reach. Fishing, golf, tennis nearby. Local folks as well as guests enjoy elaborate Sunday brunches, and the Lazy H has a cocktail bar where you can gather before dinner. Open winters for skiing and sledding.

□ Accom. for 52 guests in lodge rooms & cabins, pvt. baths. Weekly AP: A $245–$280, C (4-16 yrs.) $180–$200, incl. riding. Also daily, winter & group rates. 65 mi. NW of Denver—go N on I-25 to Rt. 66, W to Lyons, 20 mi. on Rt. 7 to ranch. Meet bus in Lyons, no chg., Denver pickup $8.50/person or $22 min. *Bill Halligan, Lazy H Ranch, Box 248, Allenspark, Colorado 80510. Tel.:(303) 747-2532. Open May–Oct. & Dec.–Apr. Area 2.*

LONGS PEAK INN & GUEST RANCH provides "mountain leisure at its best," according to the Akins. The 85-acre Rocky Mountain ranch has everything—riding, indoor gameroom, excellent food, cookouts, swimming, playground, pond fishing, outdoor games and evening activities—square dancing, movies, bingo, stage shows. It's a place for beauty and quiet, for hiking in Rocky Mountain National Park and for nearby golf, shopping, sailboating, museums, rodeos and horse shows. Conference facilities available.

☐ Lodge & guest bldgs. accom. 75 guests, all pvt. baths. Weekly AP: A $220, C $190. Daily AP: A $33, C $28. Riding extra. Also MAP rates & pkg. incl. riding. 65 mi. NW of Denver—go N on Hwy. 36 to Estes Park, S on Hwy. 7 to ranch. Meet bus in Estes Park, no chg.; train/plane in Denver, $45. *Bob & Virginia Akins, Longs Peak Inn & Guest Ranch, Longs Peak Rt. "3", Estes Park, Colorado 80517. Tel.: (303) 586-2110. Open Jun.-Sep. Area 2.*

LOST VALLEY RANCH is "beautiful and easy to get to, yet it feels quite remote with an old-time ranch atmosphere," describes a guest. "There's lots going on here—friendly guests, cordial hosts, excellent meals, with everyone having a good time." The Fosters raise quarter horses, cattle and St. Bernard dogs in a secluded valley circled by forested mountains. They enjoy sharing the naturalness of ranch life "with people who live in cement and high-rises." You'll ride scenic trails, "help" the cowboys, take an overnight pack trip, climb mountains—or enjoy the heated pool, tournament tennis courts, square dances, melodramas, hayrides, cookouts, jeep trips, staff musicals or whatever. "We serve western food," reports Bob Foster—"lots of beef, trout, barbecues and chicken." Wintertime fun means sledding through the meadow, ice skating, tobagganing, ski trips and huge open fires. Non-drinkers preferred.

☐ 20 cabins w./pvt. baths for 100 guests. Weekly AP: A $325, C 10% off to 10 yrs., babies free. Riding incl. 60 mi. SW of Denver—go 38 mi. W on US 285, S on Rd. 126 thru Buffalo to sign. Meet plane/train/bus in Denver or Colorado Springs, $50/family. *Bob & Marion Foster, Lost Valley Ranch, Rt. 2, Box F, Sedalia, Colorado 80135. Tel.: (303) 647-2311. Open all year. Area 5*

MacTIERNAN'S SAN JUAN RANCH is where Jim, Pat and their three children (late teens and 20s) settled several years ago from Montrose, where Jim taught History and Humanties. They own and lease 2,000 to 3,000 acres of meadow and mountains in the spectacular area just north of Ouray. They have horses and cows, and specialize in riding and pack trips. Fish in the stocked pond or streams, enjoy the Jacuzzi in the solar lodge, take

nature walks or go bird watching, and in winter come for sleigh rides, skating and x-country skiing. Ouray offers mountain jeeping, rafting, a hot springs pool, art shows, tennis and fine restaurants besides remarkable scenery.

☐ Accom. 20 guests—4 rooms (2 baths) & 4 apts. (pvt. baths). Weekly AP: A $250, C $195, incl. riding. Daily EP: sgl. $18, dbl. $35, C $12, riding extra. 30 mi. S of Montrose—S on US 550 to 2½ mi. below Ridgway Jct., right on dirt rd., cross bridge, left 1½ mi. to stonewall entrance. Meet plane/train/bus in Montrose, no chg. *Jim & Pat MacTiernan, MacTiernan's San Juan Ranch, Route 1, Ridgway, Colorado 81432. Tel.: (303) 626-5360. Open all year. Area 7.*

PEACEFUL VALLEY LODGE AND GUEST RANCH combines European charm and western ranch life. Step out of the Swiss-style chalet lodge into a world of riding, overnight pack trips, trout fishing. "Karl Boehm is a well-informed naturalist and horseman," notes a guest, "and an excellent host. It's a great place for families, with excellent supervision for youngsters." You won't forget a dip in the heated pool, crossing the Continental Divide by jeep to see a ghost town, scrumptious food, late kaffeeklatsches around an open fire and square dancing. Fun programs for children and teens, and indoor/outdoor arenas for horsemanship lessons. Wintertime it's x-country skiing (instruction and rentals) and 30 minutes to Lake Eldora ski area.

☐ Accom. for 160 guests in chalet & cabins, pvt. baths. Weekly AP: A $259–$287, C 1–5 yrs. less 50%, 6–9 less 30%, 10–11 les 15%. Riding incl. Conference rates Apr.–May. 50 mi. NW of Denver—take US 36 to Lyons, 15 mi. W on Rt. 7 to Rt. 72, S 3½ mi. Meet plane/train/bus in Denver, $4/person. *Karl & Mabel Boehm, Peaceful Valley Lodge & Guest Ranch, Star Rt., Lyons, Colorado 80540. Tel.: (303) 747-2582. Open all but Oct. & Nov. Area 2.*

S BAR S RANCH is a rugged working cattle ranch, nothing fancy, where you become part of the family and can help round up cattle, ride the trails, go on pack trips or attend rodeos and horseshows. A trout stream that flows past the front door is good for innertubing, too. Housekeeping cabins are adequate and not expensive, and just right for families that like planning their own activities, enjoy ranch life and appreciate staying with very friendly people. They are winterized for winter sports fans.

☐ Rustic housekeeping cabins (baths, kitchens, gas heat) accom. 4 families or groups up to 40. Weekly EP: $70/couple,

$25 ea. addl. Also daily rates. Riding extra. 170 mi. NW of Denver. From Steamboat, go 6 mi. N on Rt. 129. Meet plane/bus in Steamboat, no chg. w./ 5-day booking. *Bill & Cynthia May, S Bar S Ranch, Clark Rt., Steamboat Springs, Colorado 80477. Tel.: (303) 879-0788. Open all year. Area 2.*

Snowshoe Guest Ranch, Colorado

SNOWSHOE GUEST RANCH is an "end-of-the-road, top-of-the-mountain ranch at 9,060 feet, without such 'flatland' frills as swimming pools, tennis courts and saunas," say the Krewsons. Sharon turns out roasts, Norwegian fish cakes, beef Stroganoff and the like while Cece heads up the wrangling team and calls an occasional square dance. "We're big on horseback riding—a principal reason for coming West." Their trail rides wind through meadows, along rock ledges and into the Arapaho National Forest. From the front porch, the snow-capped mountains of the Continental Divide are visible most days, sharply etched against a bigger-than-blue sky. Sing-alongs, campfires, games, great fishing and good conversation are added attractions.

  □ Accom. 30 guests in sgl., dbl., family-sized rooms & cabins, pvt. & shared baths. Weekly AP: $163–$198; C to 6 yrs., $100–115; incl. riding. Also daily & off-season rates & "big family" disct. Winter, weekly AP: $125–$130/person. 130 mi. NW of Denver—go W to I-70, N on Rt. 9 to Kremmling, 6 mi. W on US 40, 2 mi. W on Rt. 134, right at red rock house, follow signs. Meet bus in Kremmling, no chg.; plane in Granby or Steamboat, $25, or in Denver, $50/carload. *Cece & Sharon Krewson, Snowshoe Guest Ranch, P.O. Box 237-A, Kremmling,*

Colorado 80459. Tel.: (303) 724-3596. Open all year. Area 2.

SUN VALLEY GUEST RANCH, known for its string of
Appaloosa horses, occupies a grassy meadow at 8,700 feet
surrounded by snow-capped peaks. The Brutons give lessons in
the riding arena; and trail rides, breakfast rides and pack trips of
2 to 5 days are a specialty. "We enjoyed the congeniality of the
hosts, the grandeur of the mountains and calmness of the lake,
the scent of the pines, the pack trips and the fact that no horns
were blowing and there was no smog," reports a guest. There's
lots to do: heated swimming pool, square dances, nature walks,
fishing, hayrides, steak fries. Ghost and mining towns, lake
cruises and golf nearby.

☐ 7 cabins w./pvt. baths for 30 guests. Weekly AP: A $225,
C $150–$200, (under 3 yrs., $35); C alone, $250. Riding incl. 100
mi. NW of Denver—go W on US 40 to Granby, N on US 34 to
Grand Lake, 1½ mi. W at sign. Meet bus/train/plane in Granby,
no chg. *Ken Bruton, Sun Valley Guest Ranch, Box 470-F, Grand
Lake, Colorado 80447. Tel.: (303) 627-3670. Open Jun.–Sep.
Area 2.* ·

SYLVAN DALE GUEST RANCH, 4,000 acres on the beautiful
Big Thompson River, is more than a guest ranch, explain the
Jessups, the owners and operators. "It is an authentic working
ranch with purebred cattle and horses—a great vacation experience for people of all ages in a natural, uninhibited atmosphere." They provide a heated swimming pool, Lay Kold
tennis courts, trout fishing and an indoor-outdoor recreation
complex. There are daily trail rides, breakfast rides, overnight
pack trips, arena activities and riding instruction. Mouth-
watering aromas of fresh-baked bread, cookies and pies drift
out of the "Big Kitchen." Evening is the time for group fun—
hayrides, square dances, campfire sing-alongs and more.
"Won't you join us?"

☐ Accom. 80 guests in 1-, 2- & 3-bedroom units, pvt. baths.
AP: 6 days, $165–$195, C less. Riding extra. Also daily rates. 55
mi. NW of Denver on US 34, 9 mi. W of Loveland. Meet bus in
Loveland. *Susan Jessup DeAlcazar, Sylvan Dale Guest Ranch,
2939 No. County Rd. 31D, Loveland, Colorado 80537. Tel.:
(303) 667-3915. Open Jun. thru Labor Day. Area 2.*

TRAIL'S END RANCH, set in a beautiful valley at 6,000 feet,
overlooks Grand Mesa, the largest flat-topped mountain in the
world. It is home to three generations of Hacklers who breed,
raise and train quarter horses and Appaloosas. You can help

with the horses and haying and enjoy ranch life—riding lessons, pack trips, rodeos, barbecues, hayrides, hiking, trapshooting, fishing in a stocked trout pond, gymkhana events. "Well-appointed and immaculate cabins," comments a guest, "and a handsome main lodge." Good home cooking, too, served family-style, and a weekly cookout.

☐ 6 rustic log cabins w./pvt. baths for 15 guests. Weekly AP: A $245, T $185, C $125, incl. riding. (No children under 6 yrs.) Also daily rates. 50 mi. NE of Grand Junction—go 25 mi. E on I-70, Hwys. 65 and 330, to Collbran. Meet plane/bus/train in Grand Jucntion, no chg. *Calvin & Jeanne Hackler, Trail's End Ranch, Box 202, Collbran, Colorado 81624. Tel.: (303) 487-3338. Open May–Sep. Area 4.*

VISTA VERDE RANCH is surrounded by the 1,100,000-acre Routt National Forest which has 100 lakes and 900 miles of mountain streams. With 50 horses at the ranch, trail rides and pack trips on horseback are a specialty. The ranch raises cattle, horses, hay, goats, sheep, chickens, rabbits and ducks, so meals are home-grown and homemade. Guests go on steak fries, breakfast rides, hayrides, and to trout streams, rodeos and square dances. Hand-hewn log cabins feature fireplaces, hooked rugs, calico curtains. Library and recreation room for quieter times, and special fly fishing school and pottery workshop. Ice fishing, x-country skiing and sleigh rides in winter.

☐ 6 log cabins with pvt. baths accom. 32 guests. Weekly AP: $245, C $140–$200, Sep. less. Nov.–Apr.: hskpg. units & MAP rates. 25 mi. N of Steamboat Springs—go N on Rd. 129 for 19 mi., right on Rd. 64 for 5 mi. Meet plane/bus in Steamboat, no chg.; plane in Hayden, $10/carload. *Frank & Winton Brophy, Vista Verde Ranch, Box 465, Steamboat Springs, Colorado 80477. Tel.: (303) 879-3858. Open Jun.–Sep., Nov.–Apr. Area 2.*

WAUNITA HOT SPRINGS RANCH at 9,000 feet is a guest ranch with its own hot springs pool. Horseback riding is primary, but "we have chairs on the front porch for those who wish to just do nothin'," say the Pringles. There are also jeep trips, cookouts, overnight campouts under the stars at Canyon Creek, fishing in two stocked ponds, softball and hayrides. Child care while you're off on the trail. Great for families. The Pringle boys, 17, 19 and 21, double on guitar, harmonica and bass fiddle, so there's plenty of music 'round the ranch. No drinking, and non-smokers preferred.

☐ Accom. 35 guests in comfortable (not luxurious) units w./pvt. baths. Weekly AP: A $210–$250, T $186–$198, C

Waunita Hot Springs Ranch, Colorado

$162–$174, incl. riding. Off-season & group rates. 28 mi. E of Gunnison—turn off US 50 at 176 mile marker, go 9 mi. Meet plane/bus in Gunnison, no chg. *Rod & Junelle Pringle, Waunita Hot Springs Ranch, Rt. 2, Box 56-F, Gunnison, Colorado 81230. Tel.: (303) 641-1266. Open all year. Area 5.*

WILDERNESS TRAILS RANCH, a picture-book setting in a secluded valley, offers wilderness trail rides, pack trips, trout fishing, sailing, rodeos, square dancing, staff shows, magic shows, games and trapshooting. Also a teens' program, children's counsellors, a laundromat and gift shop. "It's a perfect in-between spot," writes a guest, "not too sophisticated and yet very adequate and homey in every way. Cabins are rustic but comfortable. There's something to laugh and be cheerful about every day. The food is above average by far." In fact, the Roberts have published a cookbook of favorite ranch recipes. Their kids are 4, 8, and 16.

☐ 12 cabins w./pvt. baths for 65 guests. Weekly AP: A $235–$275, C $115–$210, incl. riding. Also daily rates. May & Sep. 10% less. 300 mi. SW of Denver; 35 mi. NE of Durango—take US 160 E to Bayfield, 28 mi. N on Vallecito Lake Rd. Meet bus/plane in Durango, $7.50/person. *Gene & Jan Roberts, Wilderness Trails Ranch, Rt. 1, Box F, Bayfield, Colorado 81122. Tel.: (303) 884-2581. [Winter: 776-C.R. 300, Durango, Colorado 81301. Tel.: (303) 247-0722.] Open May–Sep. Area 7.*

WILSON'S PINTO BEAN FARM is a real honest-to-goodness working farm run by Art and Esther Wilson and their six children (12 to 26). They grow pinto beans (of course), wheat, hay and alfalfa on 2,200 acres near Mesa Verde National Park and Four Corners. "We did everything," reports one guest, "churned butter, milked cows, ate honeycomb from the bee hives, attended a 4-H Club Fair, fed the chickens and gathered the eggs." Guests also bale hay and dig Indian artifacts, join in the activities—or just go fishing. Esther expresses the family's viewpoint: "Having guests is hard work at times," she writes, "with the never-ending pans of biscuits, etc., but I love it. After everyone's gone there's such a vacant feeling around this old farm." Their guests come from around the world.

☐ Accom. 12–14 guests in 3 dbls. & 1 sgl. in house & trailer, pvt. & shared baths. Weekly AP: A $120, T $95–$100, C $50–$75, under 4 yrs., no chg. Riding incl. Trailer weekly EP, $115. 45 mi. NW of Durango—from Cortez, go 15 mi. NW on US 666, 2 mi. W on Rd. Y, ½ mi. S on Rd. 16. Meet bus in Yellow Jacket, plane in Cortez, no chg. *Arthur & Esther Wilson, Wilson's Pinto Bean Farm, Box 252-W, Yellow Jacket, Colorado 81335. Tel.: (303) 562-4476. Open Mar.–Nov. Area 7.*

Longs Peak Inn & Guest Ranch, Colorado

Connecticut

Though the state is heavily industrialized and urbanized, New England charm still pervades much of Connecticut's countryside with its winding roads, forested hills, picturesque villages, and museums and monuments that preserve memories of a historic past. It was colonized in 1633 by settlers escaping the ironclad laws of Massachusetts. Festivals, fairs and theaters celebrate everything from dogwood to antiques to Shakespeare. Parks throughout the state provide opportunities for hiking, camping, fishing, boating and nature study. Especially scenic is the Connecticut River Valley.

CONSTITUTION OAK FARM is in a peaceful setting of woods, cultivated fields and meadows where the gentle lowing of the Holstein cows may be heard. The 217-acre dairy farm has been in the family for three generations, and the Colonial farmstead, furnished with antiques, is a haven for urbanites wanting a restful atmosphere for reading or quiet walks. "It's charming and lovely," they say. They use the refrigerator, coffee pot, toaster and dining room for snacks, and have meals in the area—at the Inn at Lake Waramaug (see next listing) for example, where they also may join in the activities.

□ Accom. 9 guests. Dbl. room w./pvt. bath, $28/night; dbl. w./shared bath, $20; sgl. w./shared bath, $10. 90 mi. N of New York City—take Thruway, Saw Mill Riv. Pkwy., I-684 & Rt. 22 to Pawling, Rts. 55 & 7 to Kent, E 5 mi. on Rt. 341, right 1 mi. on Kent Hollow Rd. (left at Y) into Beardsley Rd., farmhouse on right. *Debbie Devaux, Constitution Oak Farm, Beardsley Rd., Kent, Connecticut 06757. Tel.: (203) 354-6495. Open all year. Area 3.*

THE INN ON LAKE WARAMAUG in scenic northwestern Connecticut is where the Combs family has welcomed guests for a quarter century. Dick and Bobbie, Chris and Jeannie, Jay, Cindy and "Gram"—each has a special sphere of activity along with the friendly staff. They plan a variety of happenings—from showboat cruises around the lake to dancing lessons, barbecues, bingo, movies, slide shows and dinner dances. You can spend summer days swimming, sailing, playing tennis or golf, waterskiing, canoeing and touring the historic countryside. "It's quaint and quiet here with fantastic food," comments a guest. Come for autumn foliage, or in winter for toboganing, ice skating, x-country and nearby downhill skiing. The indoor heated pool is always open, and special feasts and celebrations greet each major holiday, year 'round.

☐ Accom. 45 guests in main house or guest houses w./fireplaces. Daily MAP: A $32–$45, dbl. occup.; discts. for 3rd person & children. Also EP rates & dinner plan, & rates for mini-vacations. Guided bus tours for groups, 1- to 3-night trips. 85 mi. N of New York City—N to I-84, exit 7, Rts. 7, 202 & 45 to lake. Meet bus in New Preston, Southbury or Kent, reas. chg. *Richard B. Combs, The Inn on Lake Waramaug, Box A, New Preston, Connecticut 06777. Tel.: (203) 868-2168 or (212) 724-8775. Open all year. Area 3.*

Florida

Ponce de Leon, the Spanish governor of Puerto Rico, came upon Florida's eastern shore in 1513. Tales of gold and a fountain giving perpetual youth drew him here, but neither he nor his successors found them. But millions have discovered a place of tropical climate, miles of beaches, 30,000 lakes, the Everglades, the Highland Hammocks and the Keys. The French, British and Spanish all took turns at ruling this territory until 1821, when the U.S. took formal possession from Spain. Florida became a state in 1845. Its wildlife is unique in the U.S., for this is the home of the alligator, crocodile, pelican and flamingo.

DeHAAN FARM. Would you like a well-equipped, air-conditioned cottage near a peaceful orange grove? There's a fruit orchard as well, plus a private lake for fishing, boating and swimming, and some riding horses. The DeHaans raise cattle, horses, pigs and chickens on their 30 acres, and when you stay there you're only 90 miles from Disney World, 30 miles from the beaches and just a few miles from famous Busch Gardens in Tampa. There's also an electric hookup and water for parking a self-contained trailer.

☐ 2-bedroom cottage w./kitchen, living room, bath, linens: $150/week EP. Trailer space, $7/day. 15 mi. N of Tampa. From I-75 take exit SR54, right 9 mi., left on Hwy. 41, right at fork, cross tracks, go 1 mi. *Quentin & Madeline DeHaan, DeHaan Farm, Rt. 1, Box 355, Lutz, Florida 33549. Tel.: (813) 949-4004. Open all year. Area 2.*

Hawaii

THE HAWAIIAN ISLANDS

Born of massive volcanoes, Hawaii's islands were not known to western civilization until 1778 when Capt. James Cook came upon them. The friendliness of the people and the beauty of the tropical islands made them a traveler's haven long before Hawaii became the 50th state in 1959. Sugar cane and pineapple grow in abundance on the six inhabited islands against a background of swaying palms and majestic volcanic mountains. The islands provide endless vacation enjoyment with their rain forests, canyons, caves, volcanic sand beaches, waterfalls, jungles, petroglyphs, boiling pots and lava casts, and every type of water and outdoor sport.

KAHILI MOUNTAIN PARK is primarily for campers who like outdoor activities, but it's not as rugged as it may sound. You sleep in all-weather tents or cabins in hotel-size beds, and after cooking and eating your meal you leave the dishes for the maid. And there's a Furo (hot Japenese bath) to ease away cares. Explore Waimea Canyon, the Grand Canyon of the Pacific, or you can climb into the rain forests of Mt. Waialeale—the wettest spot on earth. Or forsake the beaten path on backpack trips and helicopter tours through this tropical paradise. "One of the most beautiful places in the world," according to guests.

☐ Cabins & tents (central baths) for 120 guests. Daily EP for 2: cabin, $27; cabinette, $14; ea. addl., $3. Also weekly rates. 7 mi. W of Lihue. By jet from Honolulu, 21 min. *Eric & Beverly Knudsen, Kahili Mountain Park, P.O. Box 298-F, Koloa, Kauai, Hawaii 96756. Tel.: (808) 742-9921. Open all year.*

Kahili Mountain Park, Hawaii

Idaho

Picture-book words describe Idaho's scenic beauty: Hells Canyon, Sawtooth and Seven Devils Mountains, Craters of the Moon, the Snake River and the Salmon—River of No Return. All are spectacular in this land of deep, twisting canyons, wild rivers, craggy mountains and sage-covered plains. Lewis and Clark trekked through the area in 1805, and Mormons settled the rich valleys in the southeast. In the early 1860s the cry of "gold" brought a stampede of prospectors. Then silver was discovered, leading to statehood in 1890. Sheep, cattle and crops thrive here, from wheat to the famous potatoes.

BAR BQ RANCH in the Bitterroot Mountains of the northern Idaho Panhandle brings the pioneer spirit very much alive. Here you'll find complete horse-farming—plowing, mowing, raking and binding. The Jones Family raises quarter horses, Appaloosas and rodeo stock—and Belgian draft horses. What a sight when Lloyd drives an eight-horse hitch around barrels at a full trot at local exhibitions! There's a fine collection of old-time vehicles and buggies in the barns and the large indoor arena. The young Joneses (16 to 20) ride in rodeos, and young people are much in evidence here. Guests enjoy the improptu rodeos at the ranch, chuckwagon cookouts, country dances, lots of riding and (by arrangement) an extensive wilderness pack trip. The host family is described by their guests as "extremely fine people— well informed, honest, hardworking—the backbone of this country."

☐ 4 cabins w./pvt. baths for 25 guests. Weekly AP: A $200–$250, C $150, incl. riding. From Coeur D'Alene, go 40 mi.

S on US 95A, turn left at sign. Meet plane in Spokane, $40/carload; bus in Coeur D'Alene, $20/carload. *The Jones Family, Bar BQ Ranch, Box 173, Harrison, Idaho 83833. Tel.: (208) 689-3528. Open May–Oct. Area 1.*

Bar BQ Ranch, Idaho

Illinois

The Indians, the French and the English have left their mark on the names and places of this prairie state. In the Revolutionary War the Americans grabbed it, and in 1818 it became a state. The Mississippi River forms the state's western border, flowing for more than 500 miles from crop and livestock lands in the north to cottonfields in the south. The history buff can trace the route of French explorers of the late 1600s—Marquette, Jolliet, LaSalle—relive the days of Ulysses S. Grant at the historic homes in Galena, or follow the steps of Abraham Lincoln who lived, practised law, campaigned and debated all through this prairie land.

HOBSON'S BLUFFDALE is a farm covering 320 acres of majestic bluffs near the Mississippi. You can ride, explore and hike through winding woodland trails, stopping to drink at a spring. The Hobsons (their children are 15 to 23) are proud of their ancestral home and "love to share it all with you." Out back there's a large fenced yard with a treehouse and playhouse, and a barn with haymow, farm animals and pets. "A marvelous place for children—so much for them to do," a visitor writes, enthusing over the warmth and friendliness of the hosts and the generous country-style cooking. You'll also find a heated swimming pool, fishing pond, guided trail rides, pony rides, hayrides, canoe trips, cookouts, auctions, a fair and the Koster archeological digs nearby.

☐ 1- & 2-bedroom air-cond. suites w./pvt. baths accom. 33 guests. Weekly AP: A $140, C $85–$105, incl. riding. Also daily rates. 70 mi. NE of St. Louis; 50 mi. NE of Alton—go N on Rt.

Hobson's Bluffdale, Illinois

267, W on Rt. 108 to Eldred, N 4 mi. on Eldred-Hillview Rd.
Meet bus in Carrollton, no chg., train in Alton, $25/carload.
*Bill & Lindy Hobson, Hobson's Bluffdale, Eldred, Illinois
62027. Tel.: (217) 983-2854. Open May–Oct. Area 2.*

Sycamore Spring Farm, Indian

Indiana

Sand dunes along Lake Michigan, then flat prairies, and in the south, the deep valleys in the Cumberland foothills, characterize this land where the Indians lived before the dawn of history. The French settled the region in the early 1700s, but the Americans took it for their own in the Revolutionary War. By 1816 it had been carved from the Northwest Territory to form the present state, named for its Indian heritage. Corn and soybeans flourish here, and dairy and stock farms. You'll find folk festivals, county fairs, pioneer villages and museums, music and art, and such special events as maple syrup making, kite flying and pancake tasting.

SYCAMORE SPRING FARM is known not only for its herd of beefalo but for the farmhouse nestled in a pine grove and modeled after an 18th-century Williamsburg dwelling, right down to the cherry woodwork and the exposed, hand-made nails in the flooring. Here the McCoys (children 12 and 15) welcome one family or two couples at a time, an idea which developed after their own enjoyable visits at farms in Denmark. The goings-on include swimming, canoeing, fishing, and auctions or flea markets in nearby Amish country—or curling up with a good book in the library, and enjoying all kinds of home-grown and home-baked goodies at mealtime. "An elegant and charming home . . . fantastic, wonderful hosts . . . an experience we won't forget," say the guests.

  □ 2 dbl. rooms, pvt. baths, up to 8 guests. Daily AP: A $25, C $15. 150 mi. SE of Chicago; 15 mi. NW of Ft. Wayne—N on US 33 to 4 mi. past Churubusco, N on county rd. 550E for 3 mi. Meet plane/train/bus in Ft. Wayne, $10/carload. *Jerry & Janice McCoy, Sycamore Spring Farm, Box 224, Churubusco, Indiana 46723. Tel.: (219) 693-3603. Open all year. Area 2.*

Iowa

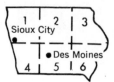

Farms cover 95 per cent of all the land in Iowa, and corn covers most of the farms. An occasional factory dots the wide prairie landscape, but mostly it's corn, soybeans, hogs, cattle and folksy small towns. The French explorers, Marquette and Jolliet, traveled here in the late 1600s, and the first settlement was established in 1788. The U.S. gained possession in 1803 through the Louisiana Purchase, and Iowa joined the Union in 1846. You'll find pioneer forts, a riverboat museum, historic Victorian homes, old grist mills, covered bridges, caves, old world colonies, Indian powwows, fairs, husking bees and hog-calling contests.

LITTLE HOUSE IN THE WOODS is a 3-story completely restored Victorian bungalow built in 1891 that accommodates two families. It's a short walk to the Koehn's 100-year-old farmhouse on a 1,000-acre dairy, beef and grain operation. Lots going on, from milking to roundup. This is Iowa's "Little Switzerland"—lush hills to hike and trout-stocked rivers and streams for swimming, canoeing and fishing. Golf and tennis nearby; also Mississippi River towns, unique craft and antiques shops, farm auctions. The Koehns invite Thanksgiving and Christmas vacationers, too, for an old-fashioned holiday with sleigh rides, ice skating, skiing and cozy fires.

☐ Fully equipped house accom. up to 8 guests. Weekly EP: $125, weekend $75. 259 mi. NW of Chicago, 80 mi. N of Dubuque. At Elkader take Postville Rd. 6 mi. N, 4 mi. W on gravel crossroad, follow signs to Big Springs. *Milford and Pat Koehn, Little House in the Woods, R.R. 1, Box 204-F, Elkader, Iowa 52043. Tel.: (319) 783-7774. Open all year. Area 3.*

Thurlow Vacation Farm, Kansas

Kansas

Long before Dorothy was obliged to see the Wizard in order to return to Kansas from Oz, this land of vast prairies was known to explorers and travelers who rolled westward in their covered wagons. When Kansas became a territory in 1854 its population stood at 700. Statehood was established in 1861. Today the awesome grain elevators rising from the flatlands symbolize the wheat supremacy of the state's prairies, and fleets of combines that harvest the sea of wheat have earned for the area its label—"Breadbasket of the Nation." Dotted across the prairies are hundreds of lakes and creeks jumping with fish.

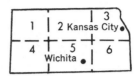

THURLOW VACATION FARM. Rod and Pearl run a typical small working Kansas farm—more modern, but otherwise not too different from the one Dorothy left for Oz. "We have no set schedules," writes Pearl, but one guest reports helping with the harvest, going to the fair and auction, just relaxing. "It was swell. The children loved it." On 160 acres the Thurlows raise wheat, milo, soybeans, oats, pigs, cattle and chickens, butcher meat, grind wheat and dehydrate foods. Their children and grandchildren run neighboring farms. Eisenhower's home, library and museum in nearby Abilene.

☐ 3 dbls., 2 baths, for 6 guests. Weekly AP: A $100, C $60–$80. 9 mi. W of Junction City & 12 mi. N. Take exit 286 on I-70. Meet plane/train/bus in Junction City, Manhattan or Topeka, no chg. *Rod & Pearl Thurlow, Thurlow Vacation Farm, Wakefield, Kansas 67487. Tel.: (913) 461-5596. Open all year. Area 2.*

Kentucky

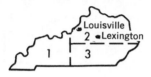

To explore this land, Daniel Boone and his party set out in 1769 through the Cumberland Gap, the only way through the mighty Appalachian Mountains. Boone's trail was used by pioneers for decades. In 1790 Kentucky, formerly part of Virginia, became a state. It rolls down from the Appalachians in the east to the Mississippi River in the west. Its central area is cave country, and to the east is the famous bluegrass region where thousands of Thoroughbred horses are raised. Its beautiful lakes were created by the damming of rivers. Kentuckians are a friendly folk with a natural ability to spin tales about their early kin.

BROWN'S VACATION FARM. Mealtimes are a parade of dishes too good to resist—"homemade everything." Between meals you're on your own to help make hay, cut tobacco, feed hogs, herd cattle, milk the cow or gather eggs. The rolling countryside invites riding, hiking, fishing, hayrides. "Fun to let the horses run—or to be alone with the trees, wind and stream," states a guest. "The Browns are now our family in Kentucky." You'll want to visit nearby attractions like Berea College, Mammoth Cave, Lincoln's birthplace, Boonesborough and various outdoor plays, and spend an evening at the Renfro Valley Barn Dance. Tennis courts nearby. Non-drinkers preferred.

☐ Accom. 8 guests in farmhouse and log cabin, pvt. baths. Weekly AP: A $120, C to 10 yrs. $80. Riding incl. Also EP rates. 60 mi. S of Lexington—go S on I-75 to Mt. Vernon exit, N on Rt. 150 about 5 mi., W on Rt. 70 for 2 mi. Meet plane/train/bus in Mt. Vernon, Berea, Somerset or Lexington, 17¢/mile. *Roy &*

Brown's Vacation Farm, Kentucky

Flora Mae Brown, Brown's Vacation Farm, Rt. 1, Brodhead, Kentucky 40409. Tel.: (606) 758-8581. Open all year. Area 2.

STRATHMERE FARM covers 229 rolling acres with a mile of frontage on the Barren River which you can explore by canoe or johnboat under towering limestone bluffs. The gregarious hosts, Jim and Linda, a former mechanical engineer and investment analyst respectively, enjoy caving, antiques, natural history, farming and sharing good conversation with urban people. You're welcome to get into the act—raising grain, hogs, goats, sheep, cows, horses and the produce of a one-acre garden. "Interesting things are going on all the time," guests say. You can ride, hike, fish, go spelunking or hunt Indian artifacts. Country auctions every Saturday. Mammoth Cave 40 miles away.

☐ 3 dbl. rooms, shared baths. A $120, C $80, weekly AP. 125 mi. SE of Louisville, 75 mi. N of Nashville. From I-65 at Bowling Green, KY, follow Rt. 231 to Scottsville, Rt. 100 beyond Fountain Run 7 mi., right on Rt. 678 for 2.2 mi., left on dirt road 2 mi. Meet plane in Nashville, $15/car. *Jim & Linda Key, Strathmere Farm, Rt. 2, Fountain Run, Kentucky 42133. Tel.: (502) 434-3652. Open Apr.–Nov. Area 1.*

Strathmere Farm, Ker

WALNUT SPRINGS FARM has 35 acres in hay, orchards and vegetables, 45 more in woods, creeks and nature trails. Livestock includes cattle, sheep, 2 horses, chickens, rabbits, barn cats, house cats ("Cougar" and "Velvet"), and a Newfoundland dog called "Kentuckee." Plenty of chores—mending fences, planting, harvesting, repairing barns and feeding animals. Supervised trapshooting, riflery, archery. "A delightful spot to enjoy farm life," reports a guest, "with very nice accommodations and hosts who are most congenial and good conversationalists." Check out the Kentucky horse park and farms nearby, the Shaker village at Pleasant Hill, Berea College, fishing lakes, swimming and golf, Marigold Fair, state and county fairs. No smoking, no drinking, preferred.

☐ One family at a time (6-8 people) accom. in 3 dbl. rooms w./2 baths. Weekly AP: A $120, C $80. 50 mi. N of Lexington, 33 mi. S of Cincinnati, Ohio—go S on I-75 to Dry Ridge exit 159, W on Rt. 22 for .3 mi., right on Rt. 467 for 2.4 mi., left on (hidden) gravel rd. for .3 mi. Meet plane in Cincinnati, no chg., or in Lexington, $10/group; train in Cincinnati, $5/group; bus in Williamstown, no chg., *Cliff & Natalie Lahner, Walnut Springs Farm, Box 9, Dry Ridge, Kentucky 41035. Tel.: (606) 824-4007. Open Jun. thru Sep. Area 2.*

WHITNEY LONGVIEW FARM covers 400 beautiful acres, part of a grant in the late 1700s to a Revolutionary soldier. Today the Tatums provide cottages with all the comforts of home for guests who come here to ride the horses, swim in the pool, go hiking or fishing or just relax. Nearby are the Barren River Reservoir and Walnut Creek Boat Dock, Mammoth Cave, My Old Kentucky Home, Lincoln Memorial, the Hermitage and "Oprey Land, U.S.A."

☐ Air-cond. cottages (4) w./2-3 bedrooms, living room, kitchen, bath; bring linens. Weekly EP: $150-$200/cottage. 110 mi. S of Louisville—go S on I-65 & Hwy. 90 to Glasgow, S on US 31E, left on rd. 1855 to farm. Meet train/bus in Scottsville or Bowling Green, no chg.; in Nashville, $10. *Browder & Clarine Tatum, Whitney Longview Farm, Rt. 2, Box 278, Scottsville, Kentucky 42164. Tel.: (502) 622-5379. Open all year. Area 1.*

Maine

The Norsemen probably sailed off Maine's rocky coast a thousand years ago, followed by Cabot and Verrazano centuries later. The English claimed the land in 1605, held on through battles with the Indians and French, left after the American Revolution, returned to fight the War of 1812, then agreed by treaty to Maine's boundary. Statehood followed in 1820. Canoeists seek out the wilderness rivers, backpackers and skiers head for the mountains, and vacationers flock to resorts and backwoods retreats on inland lakes or at the shore where picturesque ports are home to the stately windjammers.

ALBONEGON INN maintains a "determinedly old-fashioned" atmosphere on Capitol Island in Boothbay Harbor—which Pirate King John once called home port. Built more than 100 years ago, its structure is like a ship, bolted together, right where the Abenaki Indians once had clambakes on the shore. "It's a fascinating place," exclaims a guest, "a gem that lives up to its Indian translation—'pleasant meeting'." Guests are treated to nice old-fashioned rooms, furnishings of a past generation (like Tiffany lamps) and fresh-baked Maine blueberry muffins. Capitol Island, with its one-lane bridge connection to Southport, is a village corporation with its own sheriff, beaches, marinas and all.

  □ Sgl. & dbl. rooms, most w./shared baths, accom. 18 guests. Daily incl. breakfast: A $18, C to 6 yrs. $12. 10%–15% less for 1 or 2 weeks or longer. 60 mi. NE of Portland, 165 mi. NE of Boston. From Boothbay Harbor on Rt. 27, cross swing bridge to Southport, left on Rt. 238 for 1 mi., left at sign. *Roe &*

Adele Holmes, Albonegon Inn, Capitol Island, Maine 04538. Tel.: (207) 633-2521. [Sep.–Jun.: 1455 Forest Ave., Portland, Maine 04103.] Open Jul. & Aug. Area 5.

EDGEWATER MOTEL & COTTAGES on Frenchman's Bay offers guests the same things that have appealed to the Bowden family since 1790 when they received a land grant to the property. They have their own tidal pool for nature hikes— you'll find starfish, sea urchins and sand dollars. There's swimming, boating and fishing, and nearby are Acadia Park and all the attractions of the Bar Harbor area. Guests stay in rustic cottages or luxury units. "My highest recommendation," writes a vacationer, "—an unusual aura of spaciousness, comfort, quiet and privacy. It's elegant—a jewel."
    □ Accom. 75 guests in cottages & apts. w./pvt. bath & kitchen. Weekly AP: $150–$245/unit, daily $24–$40. Motel-type units, baths, kitchen & Franklin fireplace: daily EP, $38–$48 for 2. Off season rates. 40 mi. SW of Bangor, 270 mi. NE of Boston. Meet plane in Trenton, bus in Bar Harbor, no chg. *Gail & Ann Bowden, Edgewater Motel & Cottages, Box 50-A, Salisbury Cove, Maine 04672. Tel.: (207) 288-3491. Open May–Oct., (overnights, all year). Area 6.*

GOOSE COVE LODGE on Deer Isle is a naturalist's and artist's paradise—a "gem of a place," as described by one vacationer, "with walking trails winding through 100 acres of woodland and stunning views of East Penobscot Bay." It's an area of fascinating places to visit, such as quarries, canneries, lobster piers, lighthouses and Acadia National Park. The attractive main lodge of native logs with large picture windows overlooks the shore, and perched on various levels of rock are cozy cottages with fireplaces or Franklin stoves and breathtaking vistas. There's a half mile of shore frontage with safe bathing beaches, a sloop for sailing parties, smaller boats for fishing and island-hopping; also music, group singing, slide shows and a rec. hall. No pets.
    □ Accom. 60 guests in 7 isolated cottages, 10 motel units, 2 duplexes, all w./pvt. baths. Weekly AP: A $175–$245. Jun. discts. Family & daily rates. 280 mi. N of Boston; 60 mi. E of Bangor—take Tpk. To Augusta, Rt. 3 to Bucksport, Rt. 15 to Deer Isle Village, right on Sunset Rd., follow signs 3 mi. Meet plane/bus in Bangor or Bar Harbor, $20/person; in Bucksport, $15. *Joseph & Elizabeth Kern, Box F, Sunset, Maine 04683. Tel.: (207) 348-2508. Open Jun.–Sep. Area 6.*

HOMEWOOD INN on Casco Bay offers a real New England experience with the welcome given by third-generation hosts. "What a lovely place to stay," exclaims one guest. "Wood-burning fireplaces keep the cottages snug right through fall foliage time." Besides a fireplace, each pleasant housekeeping cottage has a view of the bay. Guest rooms in other buildings as well, plus a cocktail lounge and attractive dining room where seafood dishes are a specialty. The Inn has clambakes every Monday, and provides tennis, rec room, a pool, cycling, boating and fishing from the dock. Nearby: stables, golf, summer theater, Casco Bay tours, state parks and historic Yarmouth.

☐ Accom. 90 guests in rooms, suites & cottages. Daily EP: $26–$44 for 2, July.–Oct.; $22–$35 in Jun. Family & group rates. 118 mi. N of Boston. From Maine Tpk.—take exit 9, N on Rt. 1, right at Mobil Stn. & follow signs. *The Webster Family, Homewood Inn, Drinkwater Point, Box 196-C, Yarmouth, Maine 04096. Tel.: (207) 846-3351. Open Jun.–Oct. Area 5.*

KINAPIC HOUSEKEEPING COTTAGES, tucked away in a compact pine grove on a nine-mile lake in the foothills of the White Mountains, are the answer to a family's needs. Three generations of the hospitable Deutsch family are hosts. Kinapic has water sports—beach, outboards, canoes, sailboats, skiing and fishing—and clay-court tennis. Nine-hole golf and horse-riding are nearby. In the evenings the lakefront lodge is open for cards, music, ping-pong and chatting, and most of the cottages

Kinapic Housekeeping Cottages, Maine

have a fireplace to take away the chill. Interesting restaurants abound in the area. Other pastimes: hiking, auctions, summer theater, rock hunting and bird watching.

☐ Accom. 50 guests in 12 furnished cottages, all heated & w./pvt. baths, some w./living room & fireplace. Weekly EP: $145–$260/cottage, less 15% Jun. & Sep. Also daily rates. 25 mi. NE of North Conway, NH; 52 mi. NW of Portland, ME— take US 302 to Bridgton, Rt. 91 to Lovell, Rt. 5 to Kinapic. Meet plane in Fryeburg, ME, $3/person, bus in Conway, $4. *The Deutsch's, Kinapic Housekeeping Cottages, Lake Kezar, Lovell, Maine 04051. Tel.: (207) 925-1333. [Winter: (914) 478-4093.] Open Jun.–Sep. Area 5.*

McGRATH POND CAMPS is a fine place to relax, fish, go boating and see the Maine countryside. The three-mile-long pond in the Belgrade Lakes area is spring-fed. Fully-equipped housekeeping cottages, each with brick fireplace; fine sandy beach and boat landing. Small-mouthed bass, salmon, white perch and pickerel wait for fly-fishers, bait-fishers and trollers. "We enjoyed the clean, cool air and water, neat and comfortable cabins and the interesting area," observes a guest. Summer theater, fairs, horse racing and history.

☐ Accom. for 20 guests in 4 cabins w./2 bedrooms, living room, kitchen, bath, linens. Weekly EP: $65/cabin, boat incl. 194 mi. N of Boston—take I-95 exit at Rt. 137 (Waterville-Oakland) & go 5 mi. W, left at sign. *Mac & Jean McDougall, McGrath Pond Camps, Rt. 1, Oakland, Maine 04963. Tel.: (207) 465-2431. Open Jun. 15–Labor Day. Area 5.*

MOHAN COTTAGE is the place for your family if you enjoy the peace and seclusion of the Maine woods, and like getting away from town (9 miles) and having a rowboat and fishing gear and a charming, 3-bedroom fully-equipped log and stone house with a fireplace. The deck overlooks Mt. Blue State Park and an 8-acre private lake where beavers play. Fishing, blueberries, antiques, flea markets, beanhole suppers, and summer theater. 3 miles to grocery store, 7 to a restaurant.

☐ House accom. 6 guests; furnishings incl. linens. Weekly EP for 2: $150; each addl., $20. 55 mi. N of Auburn—take Rt. 4 to Farmington, left on Rt. 43 to Temple past country store, left 1 mi., right 2 mi., left on Tater Mt. Rd., 1st place on right. Meet plane in Augusta, $15/trip. *Joe & Hazel Mohan, Mohan Cottage, Temple, Maine 04984. Tel.: (207) 778-9235 or 6961. [Winter: 1954 Mt. Horeb Rd., Street, Maryland 21154. (301) 692-6832.] Open Jun. thru Dec. Area 3.*

OAKLAND HOUSE, an 1889 inn on Penobscot Bay, welcomes families from home and abroad. "This land has been in my family since granted by King George III quite a while before 1776," remarks host Jim Littlefield. "It's a super place to relax and revitalize," advises a guest; "the kids can experience a great deal of personal freedom, the food is delicious and the accommodations are clean, simple and comfortable." Lobster on the menu twice a week. Hike the trails, swim at the beaches on both lake and ocean, take in the fine view of the bay. There's a rec hall, lawn games, tennis, fishing and rowboats, and nearby golf and riding. One-week bicycle tours with guides and ocean fishing trips by arrangement.

   □ Accom. 70 guests in cottages & guest houses, pvt. & shared baths. Weekly AP: A $122–$231, C 1/3 to 1/2 less; off-season group rates. Cabin accom. 7, EP rates, 2 days min., 'til Jun. 20. 50 mi. S of Bangor. Follow Rt. 15 S 12 mi. past Blue Hill to Oakland House sign. Meet plane/bus in Bangor, $30 carload. *Jim & Sylvia Littlefield, Oakland House, Sargentville 12, Maine 04673. Tel.: (207) 359-8521. Open May–Oct. Area 6.*

ROCK GARDENS INN. Whether it's *Westview, Gray Rocks, Cool Ledge,* or any of the other six cottages which you'll call home, you're in for a delightful casual life on this rocky coast. "We're fortunate to have found such a place," advises a grateful guest who notes also the excellent food, congenial guests and hosts, and the comfortable cottages with ocean views. Just drinking in the salt air, having fresh homemade muffins in the morning, lobster cookouts on the rocks, and very good "plain homecooking" throughout your stay will be a treat. The Main Lodge has a library, and to round out activities are the 9-hole Sebasco golf course, Olympic-size saltwater pool, tennis, sailing, dances, Casco Bay boat trips, antiquing and summer theater.

   □ Accom. 50 guests in 9 cottages & 4 bedrooms in main house, pvt. & shared baths. Daily AP: A $27–$29, C $17–$19. 150 mi. N of Boston. 50 mi. N of Portland—take I-95 to Brunswick, Rt. 1 to Bath, then 12 mi. on Rts. 209 & 217. Meet plane in Portland, bus in Bath, no chg. *Dot Winslow, Rock Gardens Inn, Sebasco Estates, Maine 04565. Tel.: (207) 389-1339. Open Jun.–Sep. Area 5.*

TOWN LINE CAMPSITES, with 160 acres, offers two cabins and two camps, as well as 55 campsites for tent or trailer vacationers. It's a pleasant, rustic life on 14-mile-long

Rock Gardens Inn, Maine

Damariscotta Lake where you can fish, swim, waterski, go boating or play games in the rec room or outdoors. "We love it—think it's terrific," vacationers report. "There is privacy, and it's restful—but not so quiet as to be dull." There's lots to see and do nearby—Salt Water Recreation Areas, salt water fishing, county fairs, local Town Days, sloop races, canoe races, museums, antiques shops. Complete camper facilities include store and laundry room, firewood, ice, picnic tables, electricity, water, hot showers and steam bath.

☐ Cabins w./2 bedrooms (1 w./pvt. bath), $135/family/week. 1-room camps, $8.50/family/day. 55 campsites, $3.50+/family/day. Rates EP. 180 mi N of Boston, 20 mi. W of Rockland. On East Pond Rd. between Waldoboro & Damariscotta. *Merton & Louise Newbert, Town Line Campsites, R.F.D. 1, Waldoboro, Maine 04572. Tel.: (207) 832-5095. Open end-May thru Labor Day. Area 5.*

Maryland

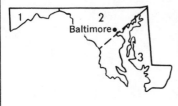

Under a land grant to Cecil Calvert, the second Lord of Baltimore, settlers came here in 1634 seeking religious freedom, a concept they protected by law in 1649. The colony repudiated the Stamp Act in 1765, the first official act of resistance to British rule, fought valiantly in the Revolutionary War, and in 1788 became the 7th state. Chesapeake Bay provides a breezy waterway for weekend sailors and fishermen. In the central area beautiful rolling farmlands provide pasture for blue bloods of the racing world. In the west the state is mountainous, with many streams.

GLENARM FARM, in the rolling hills of Middletown Valley, with views of the Catoctin Mountains and the Appalachians, offers an entire farmhouse to vacationers when the Bonds, now Chevy Chase residents, aren't using it for their holidays. It's situated in a grove of trees next to an 11-acre lake, with 174 private acres to roam. "We keep the area around the lake in park-like condition," Bill Bond mentions. "We arrange to meet guests when they arrive." We can play badminton, volleyball and horseshoes there, cook on the charcoal grill, swim, sail or fish at the lake. Much to do in the historic area—state parks, trout streams, country stores and gourmet inns.

☐ 1-family house w./3 bedrooms, bath, living room, kitchen, screened porch. Bring linens. Weekly EP: $250 Jun.–Aug., $200 spring/fall, $150 Nov.–Mar. 12 mi NW of Frederick, 12 mi. SE of Hagerstown. *Bill & Cynthia Bond, Glenarm Farm, 7004 Maple Ave., Chevy Chase, Maryland 20015. Tel.: (301) 654-2889. Open all year. Area 2.*

Glenarm Farm, Maryland

MOUNTAIN VIEW FARM, a working farm in the scenic western strip of Maryland, is up in the hills—good country for hiking and riding. The Brennemans and their 4 children (2, 7, 16 and 18) make a great hit with their guests: "The whole family is very down home, and nice to meet. Grandpa (91) is a special treat," writes a frequent visitor. Fish, canoe, have a hayride, see farming in action. Swimming and ski resorts nearby. Farmhouse can accommodate 2 families at once. Non-drinkers (or moderate) preferred.

☐ 5-bedroom farmhouse w./bath & kitchen can accom. 2 families (15 guests). Weekly EP: $150 for 4, $25/ea. addl. Daily EP: $30 for 4, $5/ea. addl. Evening meal available. 200 mi. W of Baltimore, 100 mi. S of Pittsburg. From Grantsville (22 mi. W of Cumberland on US 40), go 8 mi. S on Rt. 495 to Bittinger & phone. Meet train in Oakland, $10/carload; bus in Grantsville, $5/carload. *Harley & Joyce Brenneman, Mountain View Farm, Bittinger, Marlyand 21522. Tel.: (301) 245-4402. Open all year. Area 1.*

HIDDEN HOLLOW FARM's 115 rocky acres with beef cattle, chickens, hogs and hay lie in rolling hills between the Catoctin

Mountains and Antietam Creek. Handmade early American pieces, with four-poster beds, fireplaces and the original wide-board floors highlight the fully restored, two-story fieldstone farmhouse, circa 1800. Guests pull fish from the creek, gather fruits and vegetables, swim in the heated pool and tour country lanes and villages. They go on wagon rides, help Dr. Jim (an orthodontist) with the outdoor chores, ride the two horses (if experienced) or just relax. Frances loves "showing them around, entertaining and serving gourmet meals." Opera, ballet and history are the Abbotts' hobbies.

☐ Accom. 10 guests in air-cond. cottage for 6 & 2 dbl. rooms in main house, pvt. & semi-pvt. baths. Daily MAP/person: $15-$17 dbl. occup., $22 sgl.; EP, $8-$10 dbl., $15 sgl. Luncheon on request. 8 mi. N of Hagerstown—from I-70 take exit 35, right 4 mi. on Rt. 66, right 1.1 mi. on Rt. 64, left at blinker for 5.2 mi., right .2 mi on Strite Rd. Meet plane/bus in Hagerstown, no chg. *Dr. Jim & Frances Abbott, Hidden Hollow Farm, Rt. 8, Box 103, Leitersburg, Maryland 21740. Tel.: (301) 733-4637. Open all year. Area 2.*

Massachusetts

If the Mayflower had not run astray on the Atlantic the Pilgrims might well have landed in Brooklyn, and who knows what manner of speech might have grown from that merger. But Plymouth Rock, instead, became the cornerstone of the colony, which survived years of struggle to begin a new nation. Here disagreements with the British led to the Boston Tea Party and organization of the Minutemen. It was here in 1775 that Paul Revere made his historic ride, and at Lexington and Concord the opening volleys of the Revolutionary War were fired. In 1788 Massachusetts became a state. From the coast to the rolling Berkshire hills, history greets you at every turn.

FISKE FARM. Snug in a valley of the Berkshires, in the heart of historic New England, generations of Fiskes have operated this large dairy farm. It's near ski areas, and two miles from the Mohawk Trail. The 13-room farmhouse is the center of activities and the big kitchen is where everyone "lives" and eats. "I give Mrs. Fiske a four-star rating," exclaims a visitor, "for her beautiful land, great cooking and—most important—warm heart." You can feed the calves, see the cows milked, hike over miles of marked nature trails, or just sit under a tree and take in the beauty that surrounds you. The Fiskes will answer your questions, explain what farming is all about, and may even rout you out of bed at 4 a.m. (it's happened!) to see a calf born. The grandchildren live nearby.

  ☐ Accom. 8 guests in 3 dbls., 2 sgls., shared bath. Daily AP: A $19, C $13. 100 mi. NW of Boston, 7 mi. W of Greenfield— from I-91 go 5 mi. W on Rt. 2 to Shelburne, 1st left after

Neeley's store, 3rd farm. Meet bus in Greenfield, no chg. *Mrs. Marion S. Fiske, Fiske Farm, Zerah Fiske Rd., Shelburne Falls, Massachusetts 01370. Tel.: (413) 625-6375 or 9288. Open all year. Area 1.*

Foxhollow Resort, Massachusetts

FOXHOLLOW RESORT. Would you like a few days at an old Vanderbilt estate? Foxhollow was their Berkshire retreat. Today adults (families, too) luxuriate in this picturesque countryside. There's tennis, swimming, horseback riding, boating, sailing and golf. And in winter some of the best x-county skiing in the East. The music, theater and antiques of Tanglewood, Stockbridge and Lenox are close at hand. It's a nice mixture of formal and informal living—candlelit dining, a pleasant bar, and crackling fires in the book-lined lounge. Multi-purpose conference rooms, audio-visual equipment and catering serve conference groups in a setting free of distractions. Various special mid-week and weekend packages through the year.

◻ 4 sgl. rooms, 30 dbls., 8 suites, pvt. baths (& many fireplaces) accom. 64 guests. Daily MAP: $35–$56 weekends, $30–$46 midweek. Each addl. in dbl. room: A 25% less, C 50% less. 105 mi. N of New York City, 110 mi. W of Boston. From NYC: 85 mi. N on I-684 & Rt. 22 to Hillsdale, 10 mi. E on Rt. 23 to Great Barrington, 10 mi. N on Rt. 7. Meet plane at Bradley Airport, $10/person; bus in Lenox, no chg. *Don Altshuler, Foxhollow Resort, Lenox, Massachusetts 01240. Tel.: (413) 637-2000. Open all year. Area 1.*

THE MAPLES is a small farm inn for just 12 guests at a time, in a woodland setting of the picturesque Berkshires. You'll enjoy the swimming pool, a library full of good books and magazines, the hi-fi and piano and the music-loving guests, most of whom are here for the Tanglewood concerts and Jacob's Pillow dance programs. All agree on the excellence of the Continental-American meals prepared by Michael Alvarez, an outstanding chef. "The quality of the food and the way it was served was finer than any hotel, and I've traveled extensively," reports one. Dozens of antiques shops to supplement the cultural attractions. Overseas guests will appreciate Julia's command of Spanish and French.

☐ Inn rooms w./pvt. & shared baths for 13 guests. MAP: daily $22–$26, weekly $146–$174. 159 mi. N of NYC. From Lee on US 20 go E 14 mi. to Becket intersection, 2 mi. E on Quarry Rd. Meet plane in Pittsfield, $12/carload, bus in Lee, $10. *Michael & Julia Alvarez, The Maples, R.D. Box 23, Chester, Massachusetts 01011. Tel.: (413) 623-5353. Open Jun. thru Nov. Area 1.*

Rite-View Farm, Massachusetts

RITE-VIEW FARM spreads over 230 acres of pine grove and woodland, hay and silage, just outside historic Greenfield. If you've never seen a modern milking system where milk is piped directly from the cow to the bulk storage tank, this is the place to visit, since Ida Wright and her son have about 60 milking head of Jerseys. "An ideal base for sampling New England," recommends a group of cyclists from California. "Comfortable beds, large rooms, the smell of fresh coffee drifting up the stairs and blueberry muffins baking in the oven are a cherished memory." Swim by the dam at the old covered bridge. Family-style breakfast and dinner. Non-drinkers preferred.

☐ 3 farmhouse rooms & 1 bath accom. 10–12 guests. Daily MAP: A $17, C $12. 90 mi. NW of Boston. Take Greenfield exit 27 off I-91 ¼ mi. to Silver St., go 1 mi., right on Leyden Rd. for 2 mi. Meet bus in Greenfield, $1/person. *Mrs. Ida Wright, Rite-View Farm, 493 Leyden Rd., Greenfield, Massachusetts 01301. Tel.: (413) 773-8884. Open all year. Area 1.*

Michigan

The French missionary, Père Marquette, established a settlement at Sault Ste. Marie in 1668. The land fell into British hands, then American, and in 1808 John Jacob Astor began his fur company on Mackinac Island. This sparked development of the territory as did the opening of the Erie Canal in 1825 and the coming of the railroad. By 1837 Michigan was a state. With its upper and lower penninsulas bordered by Lake Superior, Lake Michigan and Lake Huron, the state has more Great Lakes shorefront than any other.

DOUBLE H RANCH, on the north shore of Lake Michigan with a half mile of sand beach, features horseback riding—long and short rides along the lake, in the forest and cross-country. For little cowpokes there are pony rides, swings, slides and bicycles. "It's an informal place to have the time of your life," say the Averys, "—our guests are friendly critters." They suggest a swim in the indoor heated pool, volleyball, archery and other games, boating, fishing, hayrides, barn dances and wiener roasts, "or just lazy relaxin'." In winter there's x-country skiing, snowshoeing and snowmobiling. Year 'round the racquet-ball courts, pool and sauna are open, and you can count on "hearty, family-style meals that our guests say are worth the trip."

☐ Accom. 70 guests in lodge, ranch house & beach house, mostly pvt. baths. Weekly AP: A $169–$226, T $149–$177, C 6–12 yrs., $129–$157, 1–5 yrs., $97–$125. 325 mi. N of Detroit, 60 mi. SW of Sault Ste. Marie. From I-75 take 2nd exit N of Mackinac Bridge, 22 mi. on US 2. *Carl & Beth Avery, Double H Ranch, Pecos River Trail, Brevort, Michigan 49760. Tel.: (906) 292-5454. Open all year. Area 1.*

DOUBLE JJ RESORT RANCH caters to the "Big Kids"—minimum age 18, singles and couples. With 60 riding horses and an Appaloosa breeding program it's a great place for horse activities and riding hilly, pine-covered trails on the ranch's 1,000 acres. There's also boating, tennis, canoeing, swimming, archery, baseball, volleyball and much more, with live entertainment evenings. The enthusiastic, action-oriented guests take a we're-all-in-this-together attitude which is aptly described in a slogan on the dining hall wall: "The time to be happy is now. The place to be happy is here . . ."

☐ 53 sgl. rooms & 22 dbls., pvt. baths, for about 200 guests. AP: A $235/week, $76/weekend, all-inclusive (no tipping). 20 mi. N of Muskegon—go N on US 31 to Rothbury, exit right, 1 mi. to directional signs. Meet plane in Muskegon, bus in Whitehall, no chg. *Paul & Bobbie Warsicki, Double JJ Resort Ranch, Rothbury, Michigan 49452. Tel.: (616) 894-4444. Open May–Nov. Area 4.*

Minnesota

Wherever you are in Minnesota, there is bound to be a lake nearby. More than 15,000 lakes make this a land of watery splendor, with perhaps the greatest wilderness canoe country in the world along the Canadian border. The area was explored by the Vikings in the 1300s, many historians believe. Later came the French, who ceded it to the British before the U.S. took it over and made it a state in 1858. Farming on prairies that cover half the state brings forth harvests of corn, hay and wheat and provides pasture for dairy cows, beef cattle and sheep. In winter, ice carnivals and snow sports brighten below zero days.

FAIR HILLS RESORT is the largest in the state, designed for casual family fun, with lakeside pavilion, tennis, golf, boating, heated pool, beach, fishing and pony rides. Kids play aboard a real 1936 fire engine and enjoy supervised programs. Good plain American cooking, with scrumptious Thursday smorgasbord. Also lots of mixer-style activities and good clean hi-jinx. "A genuinely friendly, wholesome resort," is a guest's description, "unashamedly corny with hootenannies and get-togethers. The large staff goes out of its way to please." Eight miles away on Fair Hills' newly acquired acreage are four luxury cabins on a 360-acre lake for fishermen who really want to "get away from it all." They'll have only the beavers, loons, muskrats, otters, deer and a pair of bald eagles for company.

☐ Cabins & rooms for 280 guests. Weekly AP: A $231; C $91–$147. 10% less early & late season. 210 mi. NW of Minneapolis—go NW on US 10 to St. Cloud, W on Hwy. 52 (I-94) to Hwy. 59N (past Fergus Falls), 2 mi. W on Rd. 31, left at Rd.

20, 1 mi. to lodge. Meet train/bus in Detroit Lakes, no chg.; plane in Fargo, $5/person ($10 min.). *Dave & Barb Kaldahl, Fair Hills Resort, Rt. 1-F, Detroit Lakes, Minnesota 56501. Tel.: (218) 847-7638. Open Jun. thru Sep. Area 1.*

HONEYSUCKLE FARM, with a lazily meandering creek, is busy, busy when it comes to the dairy operation. Corn, oats and hay grow on the 134 acres and there are chickens, pigs and farm pets to feed. "We loved the atmosphere of the old farmhouse we had to ourselves, and knew we had been right to come when our 9-year-old immediately asked, 'but where's the dishwasher?' " recalls a guest. Try your hand at milking a cow or feeding a calf. Canoe on the St. Croix River or swim at Fish Lake. Young Heinrichs range from 8 to 20 years, and there's a big family dinner every noon with home-baked bread, pies, maple syrup, vegetables and meat right from the farm. Non-smokers and non-drinkers are preferred.

☐ Accom. up to 8 guests in extra farmhouse w./4 bedrooms, bath, living room, kitchen. Weekly AP: A $125, C $80. Weekly EP: $100/group. 60 mi. N of Minneapolis—go N on I-35, E at Rush City exit thru town, continue E 1½ mi., S 1 mi., W ½ mi. Meet bus in Rush City, no chg. *Carl & Beverly Heinrich, Honeysuckle Farm, Rt. 2, Rush City, Minnesota 55069. Tel.: (612) 358-4525. Open May–Sep. Area 5.*

Missouri

Missouri once was the gateway to the West. In 1804 Lewis and Clark began their famous voyage from the banks of the Mississippi River just north of St. Louis. Here, four decades later, the wagon trains assembled for the long trek west. Two centuries earlier the French voyageurs explored the Mississippi. The French imprint in the architecture and the names of river towns still is evident. This also is Tom Sawyer and Huckleberry Finn country, and in the Ozark Mountains rivers, lakes and limestone bluffs make it a scenic vacation land. Missouri became a state in 1821.

ORGANIC ACRES is a homey place for families with small children. Ponies and horses, pigs, cows, chickens, ducks, geese and pets, plus crops and an organic vegetable garden. "It's a place to go to get away in a genuine rural setting, on the edge of one of the most beautiful woods I have ever seen," one guest reports. Ride, swim, fish, have a picnic. Hayrides and campouts. The farm cooking is tops, and you're not far from Mark Twain Cave, ball parks, fairs, bowling, skating, Mississippi River dam and ferry. Historic Hannibal an easy day trip.

    ☐ Accom. for 15 guests in ranch house rooms (shared bath), cabin & mobile home. Daily AP: A $21, C $15. 50 mi. N of Hannibal; 20 mi. S of Keokuk (Iowa)—go 15 mi. S on US 61, right on black top rd., follow signs. Meet plane in Burlington or Quincy, train in Burlington or Ft. Madison; $20/carload. *Tom & Mary Rossi, Organic Acres, Rt. 3, Kahoka, Missouri 63445. Tel.: (816) 754-6563. Open all year. Area 2.*

Montana

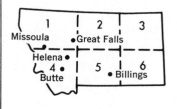

In Montana's rugged mountains and valleys, and in the plains where buffalo once grazed, sturdy pioneers established cattle ranches in the late 1800s—a proud tradition in the state today. Part of the Louisiana Purchase in 1803, Montana became a state in 1889 and is the fourth largest in the nation. Fur traders, missionaries, explorers (beginning with the Lewis and Clark Expedition in 1805), gold and silver mining and Indian troubles all have carved their place in the state's history. It contains vast wilderness areas, national forests, wildlife ranges, 100 ghost towns and Glacier National Park, and borders Yellowstone.

BLACKTAIL RANCH, 10,000 acres near Scapegoat Wilderness, was homesteaded in 1886. It's at 5,000 feet elevation between Yellowstone and Glacier Parks, and features riding, fishing, swimming, spelunking, campouts, pack trips and covered wagon rides to an ice age cave. "Enjoyed riding and roaming and exploring," writes a guest. "Hosts are warm people. A place for guests who like farm life and rugged ranch living. As for us—we're going back!" Small museum of Indian artifacts right on the ranch (and small fee).

☐ 3 cabins (1 very rustic), pvt. baths, accom. 8–12 guests. Daily AP: A $40, C $20, incl. riding. Pack trips, A $60, C $30, per day. Walking trips with packstock, $45/day. 55 mi. N of Helena. From Wolf Creek go 15 mi. NW on Rt. 434, 3 mi. left on gravel rd. Meet plane/train/bus in Great Falls, $25/family. *Tag & Lyla Rittel, Blacktail Ranch, Wolf Creek, Montana 59648. Tel.: (406) 235-4330. Open May–Dec. Area 1.*

CANYON RANCH. The Smith River, famous for trout, winds through this 6,500-acre working cattle ranch for four miles, flowing on into a cliff-walled gorge. Join the Ziegs in the day's activities—riding, working cattle, haying, fencing, feeding and calving. A guided fishing float or pack trip can be arranged—or you can paint, read a book or listen to music. Savor Janet's old-fashioned cooking, homemade bread and butter—or manage on your own in housekeeping cabins. The Ziegs' interests include history, music, art, sports, photography, travel, crafts and current events. "We had a terrific vacation," recalls one guest. "We rode, fished, worked, loafed, visited—all at our own pace. A memorable experience."

☐ Cabins & ranch house rooms, pvt. & shared baths, for 14 guests. Weekly AP: $161–$196, C $140–$147; EP: A $91–$105, C $84–$98. C alone $245 AP. Riding incl. Fishing, pack & float trips extra. 185 mi NW of Billings. From White Sulphur, 15 mi. W on Rt. 360, N on gravel rd. Phone first. Meet plane in Helena or train in Livingston, $15/person or $30/carload; bus in White Sulphur Springs, $10/carload. *George & Janet Zieg, Jr., Canyon Ranch, R.R. 1, White Sulphur Springs, Montana 59647. Tel.: (406) 547-3502. Open Jun. thru Oct. Area 4.*

CIRCLE EIGHT RANCH at 5,100 feet adjoins the Lewis & Clark National Forest and Bob Marshall Wilderness. The Teton River flows through the 3,000-acre horse ranch, its brand registered in 1889 by Ken's pioneering grandparents. The hospitality and western traditions of this old-time outfit carry on today. No more than 20 guests at a time, some from as far away as Scotland and Denmark. "It was fantastic," exclaims one guest, "everyone was so helpful!" You'll enjoy fine horses, beautiful trails, stream and lake fishing, heated swimming pool and attractive, comfortable log cabins. Weeklong wilderness pack trips (extra) into fabulous high country are "beyond compare."

☐ Accom. 20 guests in cabins w./pvt. bath, fireplace & electric heat. Weekly AP: A $220, C under 8 yrs. 10% disct. Riding incl. 85 mi. NW of Great Falls; 26 mi. NW of Choteau—go N on US 89 for 5 mi., left 17 mi., right 1½ mi. beyond mtn. guard stn. to signs. Meet plane in Great Falls, $40/carload; bus in Choteau, $5. *Ken & Alice Gleason, Circle Eight Ranch, Box 457-A, Choteau, Montana 59422. Tel.: (406) 466-2177. Open Jun.-Sep. Area 1.*

FLATHEAD LAKE LODGE & QUARTER CIRCLE LA RANCH covers 2,000 mountain acres on a wooded lakeshore. "Be part of the West—live it and enjoy the most friendly vacation you ever had!'' urge the Averills. Ginny and Les and their 7 sons are "the finest people we know," comments a guest. "This is good, wholesome recreation in a friendly family atmosphere." The hosts' teenagers keep things humming—ranch life and horseback riding combined with all kinds of lake sports—water-skiing, sailing, cruiser trips, canoeing and fishing. And there's a heated pool, plus tennis, steak fries, songfests. Near Glacier National Park and a golf course.

□ Accom. for 90 guests in family cottages & lodge rooms, all pvt. baths. Weekly AP: A $294, T $262, C $217, (to 4 yrs., $63). Riding incl. Also daily rates. 18 mi. S of Kalispell; 100 mi. N. of Missoula—go W on I-90, N on Rt. 200 to US 93 to Rt. 35 to 1 mi. S of Bigfork. Meet plane in Kalispell, train in Whitefish, bus in Big Fork, no chg. *Les & Ginny Averill, Flathead Lake Lodge & Quarter Circle LÂ Ranch, Bigfork, Montana 59911. Tel.: (406) 837-4391. Open May–Sep. Area 1.*

FORD CREEK RANCH occupies a remote valley with a trout stream, and the mountains of the Lewis and Clark National Forest on all sides. "Guests are essential to our social life," writes licensed outfitter Liz Barker, and she and her two grown children host them right at the ranch or pack them into the mountains. "The friendly manner of the staff was memorable," writes a guest, "and during our five days in the Rockies we caught all the spotted trout we could eat." Wildflowers, geologic wonders, and wildlife abound for the amateur naturalist and photographer. The ranch itself has 35 horses and mules, plus two housekeeping cabins for guests 20 feet from the creek, with the bathhouse just over the bridge.

□ Log cabin w./shared bath, & A-frame w./pvt. bath, accom. 11 guests. Weekly EP: $175 & $225. Riding extra. 75 mi. W of Great Falls—go W on I-15 to Vaughn, W on Rt. 200 to Simms, W on Rt. 21 to Augusta, W on Benchmark Rd. 18 mi. Meet plane/bus in Great Falls, $10/person. *Liz Barker, Ford Creek Ranch, Box 329-R, Augusta, Montana 59410. Tel.: (406) 562-3672. Open May–Sep. 10. Area 1.*

HALTER RANCH involves 50,000 acres of meadow, wild range land, badlands and fantastic formations in the Missouri River Wilderness Waterways area—a 120-mile stretch of river that's still like Lewis and Clark saw it. Here the Halters raise cattle, horses, hay and grain, and you can take part in roundups, brandings and other operations at various times. There's lots to do—horse rides, pack trips, a boat trip on the Missouri, four-wheel-drive treks to historic P N Ranch, trips to old gold mines (now reopened "because there's still gold in them thar hills"), to sites of old Fort Chardon and Fort Claggutt, and to the Little Rockies where you'll visit ghost towns—Landuski or Zortman, the stamping grounds of Kid Curry and the Wild Bunch, the last train robbers. The Old West is still here.

☐ Bunkhouse & 4 ranch house rooms for 10 guests, shared baths. AP rates: daily, A $35, C $25; weekly, A $210, C $150. Incl. riding & 2-day pack trip. 80 mi. NE of Great Falls on US 87. Meet train in Havre, $15; plane in Great Falls, $25; bus in Big Sandy, no chg. *Gay Pearson, Halter Ranch, Big Sandy, Montana 59520. Tel.: (406) 386-2464. Open Apr.–Nov. Area 2.*

HELL CREEK GUEST RANCH covers 20,000 acres of Missouri River Badlands, where the Trumbos (two teenage children) raise wheat, barley, oats, cattle, sheep, hogs and other animals, including a milk cow. "Guests go along with us in our daily work," John explains, "and that way they get to see the scenery as well as how we care for our livestock." The "scenery" involves colored formations and precipitous topography that was a lush tropical paradise 70 million years ago. The remains of fossilized animals are abundant. "Our guests some-

Canyon Ranch, Montana

times find fragments of duckbilled dinosaurs or turtles, and crocodile and shark teeth," John reports. "Two of the largest known fossilized triceratops were found four miles from the ranch house." Abundant wildlife and waterfowl in the area, fishing and swimming in Fort Peck Lake; neighborhood brandings in June.

☐ Cabin & pvt. bath for family w./1-4 children, $500/week AP, incl. riding. 121 mi. NE of Billings—go N on US 87 to Grassrange, E on Rt. 200 to Jordan, N 10 mi. on Hell Creek State Park Rd., left 1½ mi., right on ranch rd. Meet plane in Billings, $100/carload. *John & Sylvia Trumbo, Hell Creek Guest Ranch, Box 325, Jordan, Montana 59337. Tel.: (406) 557-2224. Open Jun. thru Sep. Area 3.*

HIDDEN HOLLOW, just two miles from the Missouri River and surrounded by grassland and wheat farming strips, gives vacationers a chance to enjoy the ranch (horses and a few cattle and pigs) and at the same time explore this historic area. The Gierkes are involved with the local school winters (Elsie teaches) and welcome one family at a time into their home in summer. You can ride with them on their 13 acres and the adjacent 300-acre ranch—"I rode a horse before I could walk," Elsie says—see where they find fossilized tortoises, visit the museum and art gallery and take a river cruise. It's a fascinating area.

☐ Accom. 1 family in 3 bedrooms, shared bath. Daily AP: A $25, C $15. 50 mi. NE of Great Falls, 75 mi. SW of Havre. From Fort Benton take Geraldine Hwy. E 3 mi., left on gravel rd. 1 mi., right 1 mi. down coulee. Meet plane in Great Falls, $10/carload; train in Havre, $15; bus in Ft. Benton, no chg. *Earl & Elsie Gierke, Hidden Hollow, Box 1107, Fort Benton, Montana 59442. Tel.: (406) 622-5301. Open Jun.-Aug. Area 2.*

LAZY AC RANCH spreads over 4,000 acres of mountain and rolling pasture adjoining the Helena National Forest where the Craigs run horses and cattle. It's relaxing and peaceful, whether you're viewing the majestic country on horseback or sitting by the crackling fire in your cabin or the lodge. The lodge is one center for activity—good wholesome meals, square dances, pool, ping pong and conversation—and the corral is another, with lots of backcountry trail riding and ranch rodeos. And there's fine fishing in lakes and blue ribbon rivers and streams. "The welcome mat is always out," say the hospitable Craigs.

☐ Accom. 24 guests in triplex cabins, pvt. baths. Weekly AP: $240-$250/person. 50 mi. S of Helena—S on US 287 to

Leffingwell's G Bar M Ranch, Montana

Townsend, E 20 mi. on Rt. 12, right 1 mi. on Grassy Mt. Rd.
Meet plane in Helena, $15/carload, train in Livingston, $25, bus
in Townsend, no chg. *Arlie & Millie Craig, Lazy AC Ranch, Box
460, Townsend, Montana 59644. Tel.: (406) 547-3402. Open
Jun. 15–Sep. 15. Area 4.*

LEFFINGWELL'S G BAR M RANCH, a 3,300-acre working
cattle ranch in the Bridger Mountain foothills, is ten miles east
of the Ski Bowl. It has been in the same family since 1904, and
grandchildren of early guests now come with their own kids.
"Most of the riding is done in connection with the cattle work,"
the hosts explain. "We check fences and water holes, doctor
calves, and pack salt to cattle on summer range in the high country." Highlights include supper rides and fishing, rock and fossil
collecting, all-day rides and steak fries. Saturday night it's
music. "There's no better place anywhere," says a guest, "a
genuine ranch with the accent on horses, good accommodations,
hospitality and great meals"—which include Mary's famous
sourdough hotcakes.
   □ Accom. 14 guests in 2 cabins & 4 dbls. in ranch house, pvt.
baths. Weekly AP: A $185–$210, C $157–$176, incl. riding. 27
mi. NE of Bozeman—take Bridger Ski Bowl rd. past ski run
turnoff, right on Clyde Park fork 6.4 mi. Meet plane/train/bus
in Bozeman, no chg. *The Leffingwells, Leffingwell's G Bar M
Ranch, P.O. Drawer AE, Clyde Park, Montana 59018. Tel.:
(406) 686-4687. Open May–Sep. Area 5.*

LONE MOUNTAIN RANCH was started in the 1920s, long before Chet Huntley discovered it and developed nearby Big Sky. The Schaaps (3 children, 9 to 20) raise horses on the secluded 3,340 acres bordered by the Spanish Peaks Primitive Area. Spacious log cabins with open fireplaces and wood-burning stoves house guests, who gather at the main lodge and rec room for meals, music, slide shows and a small bar, and at the heated pool. Both easy and rugged trails, a horse for each guest, and a guide for every seven riders. Also naturalist-guided walks. In winter Bob and Viv are great ski touring enthusiasts. "It's the most exciting touring in the country," they say, "—dry powder snow, terrain from level to very steep, 35 miles of groomed trails and 300 miles of wilderness trails." He provides certified instruction, rentals, a guide for every 7 skiers and arranges trips into Yellowstone.

□ Accom. 45 guests in 15 cabins, pvt. baths. Weekly AP: $267–$377 for 1–4 persons, $202 ea. addl. Also family, daily & off-season rates. 40 mi. S of Bozeman, 47 mi. N of West Yellowstone; from Rt. 191, 4 mi. W thru Big Sky Resort, right at sign. Meet plane/train/bus in Bozeman, $25/carload. *Bob & Viv Schaap, Lone Mountain Ranch, P.O. Box 145-A, Big Sky, Montana 59716. Tel.: (406) 995-4644. Open all but 6 wks. in Apr.–May & 8 wks. in Oct.–Dec. Area. 4.*

NINE QUARTER CIRCLE RANCH is a place to "rough it" with all the comforts of home, 7,000 feet high in the Rockies. The ranch is surrounded by wilderness and unspoiled trout waters, and near Yellowstone, ghost towns and old gold mines. There are 120 Appaloosa horses, and you're on one much of the time—sometimes on a 2-day pack trip. There's a glorified swimming hole, square dances, barbecues, day and overnight rides, movies, playground and babysitters. "We leave counting down the days until we can return" echoes a typical guest reaction to the genuine hospitality of the Kelseys. Special fly fishing school in September in the "Magic Circle"—headwaters of great streams.

□ Accom. 80 guests in 35 family log cabins w./pvt. bath, wood-burning stove & maid service. Weekly AP: A $263–$300, C $184–$237, incl. riding. Before Jul. 22, 10 days: A $297, C $238. Fly fishing school, $273. 33 mi. N of W. Yellowstone on Hwy. 191, 5 mi. W on Taylors Fork. Meet plane in W. Yellowstone, $12/person ($50 max.). *Howard, Martha & Kim Kelsey, Nine Quarter Circle Ranch, Gallatin Gateway, Montana 59730. Tel.: (406) 995-4276. Open Jun. thru Sep. Area 4.*

ROONEY RANCHES spread across 9,600 acres of hills and open country with pine, cedar, wildlife, wheat, hay and about 500 Hereford cattle. Jim, Penne and their four-year-old are hosts at one ranch, and his parents and teenage sisters at the other. "Grandfather" homesteaded the property. "It's a place for families to become closer with no outside pressures," Jim explains. You'll do whatever they're doing—haying, greasing windmills, rounding up cattle, branding, breaking horses, building corrals and windbreaks, repairing fence, cutting trees for posts, checking water holes and fighting forest fires. Or you can ride, go on a jeep trip, paint, hike, photograph, fish or relax. At practice sessions on the ranch for area rodeos you learn to bulldog a steer, tie up a calf and all—though you may just watch. In winter—cattle feeding and snow activities. Sundays the Rooneys go to church.

   □ Apt. w./2 bedrooms, living room, kitchen, bath at each ranch. Daily AP: $20/family member, $25/sgl. Trailer sites incl. activities, no meals, $20/day for 2. 200 mi. E of Billings, 45 mi. S of Miles City—Rt. 312 S to 37 mi. marker, right on gravel rd. 7 mi. Meet plane in Billings or Rapid City (South Dakota), $60/carload; or in Miles City, no chg. *Jim H. & Penne Rooney, Rooney Ranches, Broadus Stage, Miles City, Montana 59301. Tel.: (406) 421-5551 or 784-2770. Open all year. Area 6.*

SIXTY THREE RANCH promises "you'll eat heartily, sleep soundly and be as active or relaxed as you please." It's a 2,000-acre working stock ranch at 5,600 feet in spectacular Mission Creek Canyon of the Absaroka Mountains. Every day there are trail rides into an area of rushing waterfalls snow-capped peaks and mountain lakes. "I'd never ridden before and it was great fun," advises a guest, "especially good for new riders as no one made me look ridiculous!" Good food, good company, beautiful country—is how another sums it up. Fishing, hiking, fossil hunting, pond swimming or just loafing compete for your time. On pack trips (by arrangement) you ride scenic trails to ghost towns, old mines or a glacier imbedded with age-old grasshoppers. The ranch day starts with the aroma of hearty breakfasts. "But don't hurry," reassures Jinnie. "Let the kids stampede to the lodge to pile into the pancakes with new friends. You can take your own sweet time." She and daughter Sandra operate the ranch.

   □ Accom. 32 guests in cabins for 1-12, pvt. baths. Weekly AP: A $235-$280, C $220-$245, incl. riding. 120 mi. W of Billings—from Livingston go 12 mi. SE on Swingley Rd. Meet plane

Sixty Three Ranch, Montana

in Billings, $60/carload, or Bozeman, $25; train/bus in Livingston, no chg. *Virginia Christensen & Sandra McCune, Sixty Three Ranch, Box 676-V, Livingston, Montana 59047. Tel.: (406) 222-0570. Open Jun.–Sep. Area 5.*

SWEET GRASS RANCH is a rustic stock ranch in a beautiful valley of the Crazy Mountains with a stream meandering past the cabins. "Warm memories of our guests keep flowing in," Shelly writes, "like rafting on a mountain lake, cowboy boot skiing on August snow banks, helping to fight fires, repairing flood damage, pulling cows out of bogs and working cattle drives." For guests it's a vacation "surpassing expectations, with fantastic hosts, great for families." The young Carroccias are 6 to 15. Endless miles of riding (pack trips and moonlight rides, too), hiking, fishing, branding, rodeos, campouts, steak and fish fries, seeing ghost towns and buffalo jumps.

☐ Accom. 30 guests in cabins (central bathhouse or pvt. baths) & lodge (shared baths). Weekly AP: A $190–$220, C $175–200, incl. riding. 121 mi. W of Billings, 40 mi. NW of Big Timber, on I-90. Meet plane in Billings, $40/carload; train in Livingston, $30; or bus in Big Timber, no chg. *Bill & Michele Carroccia, Sweet Grass Ranch, Big Timber, Montana 59011. Tel.: (406) 537-4477. [Winter: (406) 537-4497.] Open Jun.–Aug. Area 5.*

Nebraska

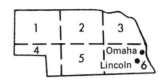

Windmills dot the landscape of Nebraska's prairies and undulating Sand Hills region, filling watering holes for the livestock or for irrigating fields of grain. Have you ever visited a town with "Population—140" on its sign? Nebraska is full of such neighborly places, with Main Streets that are one block long. Covered wagon tracks can still be found on the Overland Trail, the route of pioneers to the California goldfields in the mid-1800s. Spain and France once laid claim to this territory. It was acquired by the U.S. as part of the Louisiana Purchase in 1803.

PINE HILLS RANCH is a working 1,100-acre cattle ranch with a spring-fed creek in scenic pine country where wheat and alfalfa grow. It's a quiet scene. Children fish and become acquainted with cows, pets, deer, wild turkey and play with their hosts' young cousins. Guests join in ranch activities, collect rocks and Indian artifacts, go to cattle auctions, make day trips to Mt. Rushmore, the Badlands and the Black Hills and sometimes have a chance to observe Indian sun dances. They speak of their hosts as "fine people who go out of their way to do things for you—most hospitable and friendly."

☐ Accom. 10 guests in sod house (modernized) & 2 ranch house rooms, pvt. baths. Weekly AP: A $120, C $85. Daily AP: A $20, C $15. 400 mi. NW of Omaha, 14 mi. NE of Rushville. Meet plane in Chadron, bus in Rushville, no chg. *Alan & Kathleen Harris, Pine Hills Ranch, Rt. 1, Box 30, Rushville, Nebraska 69360. Tel.: (308) 327-2762. Open all year. Area 1.*

Nevada

Nevada is a land of deserts, mountains, cattle, sheep, mines—some of them now eerie ghost towns—and gambling casinos. At night the brilliantly lighted Las Vegas "Strip" gleams across a blackened desert like a legendary spaceport. Once a part of the Utah Territory, Nevada became a state in 1876. The Mormons established its first permanent settlements. So desolate was this rugged country of sagebrush and cacti that camels were tried for hauling supplies to the mines. Only after irrigation projects were developed did the rich soil produce crops. Cattle and sheep graze here on some 55-million acres of rangeland.

NIXON RANCH is the home of LaRue (born there), Sterling (retired Air Force pilot), and Thayne and Coleen (son and daughter-in-law). They raise crops, chickens, ducks, cows and graze 1,000 head of cattle on 13,000 acres. "We want to get to know people from other places," LaRue writes, "and want others, especially young people, to understand more about ranch life." Branding cattle, roundups, cattle drives, feeding the animals, planting and harvesting are among the activities they'll offer guests. And swimming in the large reservoir or "a lovely warm springs." In winter you'll go bobsledding and x-country skiing, then pop corn and warm up by the wood stove. The Nixons complete a three-year L.D.S. mission in Spain in July and will be ready for guests by September, 1979.

☐ Accom. 11 guests in 3 rooms & bunkhouse for 4, w./2 shared baths. Weekly AP: A $125, C $75, incl. riding. 180 mi. W of Salt Lake City (Utah), 60 mi. E of Elko—from I-80 exit at Wells, at light in center of town go N 9 mi., 1st ranch on right.

Meet plane in Elko, $20/carload; train/bus in Wells, $5/carload. *Sterling & LaRue Nixon, Nixon Ranch, Metropolis, Wells, Nevada 89835. Tel.:(702) 752-3861. Open all year. Area 2.*

Nixon Ranch, Nevada

New Hampshire

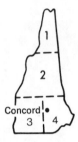

The British settled this land in 1623, and after much conflict over land grants, the Crown decreed it to be a separate province. It was the first of the colonies to adopt an independent government, and the ninth to become a state (1788). In the 19th century, New Hampshire changed gradually from an agricultural to an industrial state, with its swift rivers powering mills and factories. In its White Mountains ski and summer resorts are filled with happy throngs who consider this ideal vacation country at any time of year.

INN AT EAST HILL FARM mixes resort and farm life on 300 acres of rural mountain scenery. "For us it's the perfect vacation," comments one family. "We love the outdoors and hominess—fires going—family-style country cooking—the beautiful Monadnock setting." Guests have been coming back to this rustic scene for 30 years. There are saddle horses, farm animals, trail rides, outdoor and indoor heated pools, a rec room, square dancing, boating pond, fishing, mountain climbing, tennis, sauna, children's program, teen activities and adult parties. If that's not enough, nearby are a lake, private beach, speedboat rides, waterskiing and canoeing, theaters, churches, auctions and golf. Or you can just day-dream in the shade of a tree.

☐ Inn rooms & cottages w./2–3 bedrooms & pvt. baths for 60 guests. Weekly AP: $580 for family of 4, addl. child, $90. Winter weekend AP: A $62, C $46. Also daily rates. 210 mi. N of NYC—take I-95 to I-91 to Rt. 9 E to Keene, Rt. 12 S to Troy, left after center. Meet plane in Keene, bus in Fitzwilliam, Jaffrey or Troy, no chg. *The Adams Family, Inn at East Hill Farm, Troy, New Hampshire 03465. Tel.: (603) 242-6495. Open Jun.–Oct. & Dec. 26 thru Feb. Area 3.*

PEASE'S SCENIC VALLEY is a 14-acre farm where you're welcome to move in with the family (children are 10 to 16) and share the modern ranch-style house which Jerry has built. There are cows, pigs, steers, heifers, chickens, horses, dogs and cats in Jerry's barn and down the road at Grandpa Pease's 300-acre dairy farm. Toni's home cooking uses the farm's meats, vegetables, milk and butter. You can help with the haying or sugaring, pick berries, churn butter, swim and fish in the ponds or hike the Appalachian Trail. It's a scenic area for touring, with villages and antiques shops. In winter there's skiing, bobsledding, sleigh rides and ice skating.

☐ Guest rooms (3), share family bath; (or sleep in tent or hayloft). Daily AP: $20/person. Also weekly rates. 24 mi. N of Hanover—N on Rt. 10, 10 mi. E on Rt. 25A. *Jerry & Toni Pease, Pease's Scenic Valley, R.F.D., Orford, New Hampshire 03777. Tel.: (603) 353-9070. Open all year. Area 2.*

Pease's Scenic Valley, New Hampshire

PURITY SPRING RESORT, in a lovely setting of the White Mountains, is perfect for families. The Hoyt Family has operated the wonderful, old-fashioned inn for nearly half a century. "Very warm and personal hospitality and good food in generous quantities are among the outstanding features of this resort," writes a guest. You'll find a private lake, boats, water-skiing, tennis, craft shop, square dancing and breakfast cook-outs over a morning campfire on Mondays. The inn stays open through fall foliage season, and opens up again for Christmas guests. It's always booked summer weekends, but try mid-week—you might get in even without much advance notice.

☐ Accom. 100 guests in 36 rooms (most w./pvt. bath) & 3 dbl. cottages. Daily AP: A $21-$30, C 50% off, to 2 yrs. free. Weekly AP, 10% less. Groups (15 or more), 10% disct. 116 mi. NW of Boston. 60 mi. NW of Portsmouth—take Spaulding Tpk. & Rt. 16 to Center Ossipee, Rt. 25 E to Effingham, Rt. 153 N 6 mi. to East Madison. Meet plane in Portland (ME), $20 for 1, $5 ea. addl.; bus in Conway, $4 for 1, $1 ea. addl. *The Hoyt Family, Purity Spring Resort, East Madison, New Hampshire 03849. Tel.: (603) 367-4648. Open Jun.-Oct. & Dec.-Mar. (All yr. for groups.) Area 2.*

ROCKHOUSE MOUNTAIN FARM INN. If you wonder why the guests are smiling, it's because they're content that some folks don't know about this beautiful farm which families have been enjoying for 32 years. "We want to tell the world at one moment—then keep it a secret the next," one of them says. This mecca in the foothills of the White Mountains is open summer and fall, situated on 350 acres. A private beach on Crystal Lake handles water buffs. Help with the milking, haying or other chores, ride the wooded trails on Rockhouse saddle horses, fish or just fiddle around. The Edge Family offers the kind of warm hospitality that makes guests say, "We can hardly wait to come back again!" Non-smokers are preferred.

☐ Accom. for 45 guests, some w./pvt. baths. Daily MAP: A $25-$28. Special weekly rates & disct. for young people. 50 mi. W of Portland, 125 mi. N of Boston. From Conway, S on Rt. 153 to Eaton Center, right after Post Office & ½ mi. on left. Meet bus in Conway, no chg. *The Edge Family, Rockhouse Mountain Farm Inn, Eaton Center, New Hampshire 03832. Tel.: (603) 447-2880. Mid-Jun.-Nov. Area 2.*

SNOWVILLAGE LODGE is "the place I return to when I daydream myself the perfect spot," writes a frequent guest. You'll find a European atmosphere, gourmet meals, books and music, dogs and cats, fireplaces and coziness, birds, tranquility and spacious rooms with views of the Presidential Range of the White Mountains. There's a tennis court, hiking paths, swimming at a private lake, and resort activities 15 minutes away. Running the inn is a way of life for the Blymyer family (with two daughters)—a pleasant change from their years of work in films. In winter they have a cross-country ski school, instruction, trails and rentals, and nearby are downhill ski areas.

☐ Accom. 28 guests, rooms w./pvt. baths. Daily MAP: $28-$30/persons, dbl. occup. Also sgl., weekly, mid-week &

family rates; group & club rates. 130 mi. N of Boston, 8 mi. S of Conway—S 5 mi. on Rt. 153 to Crystal Lake, left 1½ mi. Meet plane in Portland, $15/carload; bus in Conway, no chg. *Patrick & Ginger Blymyer, Snowvillage Lodge, Snowville, New Hampshire 03849. Tel.: (603) 447-2818. Open all year. Area 2.*

Snowvillage Lodge, New Hampshire

New Mexico

The Pueblo Indians sometimes permit spectators to watch their ceremonial dances. In another part of the state, at White Sands, space-age missiles are launched. New Mexico, fifth largest among the states, displays great contrasts stemming from its Indian, Spanish, Mexican and space-age heritage. Once a province of Mexico, it was ceded to the U.S. in 1848. But not until 1912, after the Santa Fe Railroad brought in modern machinery and a mining boom began, did it become a state. Mountainous areas provide a lofty setting for ranches and lodges, where you can fish, ride, ski or visit Indian pueblos.

BEAR MOUNTAIN GUEST RANCH adjoins the Gila National Forest. Here Myra, devoted to plant identification and birding, welcomes guests at the homey, rambling, pueblo-style structure built in the 1930s. "Breakfast is in the bird watching room" a guest writes. Myra cooks and serves it, "flapjacks in one hand, binoculars in the other. Catalogs of southwestern birds and plants surround the diners, and all action may come to a halt when a bridled titmouse stares back in the window." The food is good, rates reasonable, rooms comfortable and baths antique but functional, guests say. "I was enthralled with Myra and her store of knowledge," one adds. The area abounds with birds, mammals, lizards and plants not found in other regions, and there are the Gila cliff dwellings and Kwilleylekia ruins to observe, and much more.

☐ Accom. 25 guests in main house, guest house & cottage, pvt. baths. Daily AP: approx. $20–$30 ea. for 1–5 persons. Group discts. & EP cottage rates. 247 mi. SW of Albuquerque, 4 mi. N of Silver City. Meet guests at Silver City airport, Deming or Lordsburg, $4-$8/person, Silver City bus, 50¢. *Myra B. McCormick, Bear Mountain Guest Ranch, P.O. Box 1163-F, Silver City, New Mexico 88061. Tel.: (505) 538-2538 (ask for Myra). Open all year. Area 3.*

LOS PINOS RANCH. You'll spend your time riding, fishing, hiking, loafing and devouring Alice's gourmet cooking at this summer guest ranch in the heart of the Sangre de Cristo Range in Santa Fe National Forest. They guide special pack trips and daily rides into Pecos Wilderness, and all guests get horsemanship instruction before setting out. "The home cooking and baking is surpassed only by the natural beauty of the high mountain surroundings," rhapsodizes a vacationer. Another praises the spaciousness and comfort of the rustic cabins. Many birds and wildflowers, but "no poisonous snakes or scorpions, and mosquitoes are rare." Historic sites, Indian pueblos and nearby parks to visit by car on day trips.

☐ 4 rustic cabins w./pvt. baths for 18 guests. Weekly AP: A $168, C $17–$112. Daily AP: A $30, C $3–$20. Riding extra. 45 mi. NE of Santa Fe on Rt. 63. Meet plane in Albuquerque, $30/carload; train in Lamy, $15; bus in Santa Fe, $15, or in Pecos, $10. *Bill & Alice McSweeney, Los Pinos Ranch, Box 8, Rt. 3, Tererro, New Mexico 87573. Tel.: (505) 757-6213. [Nov.–Apr.: 13 Craig Rd., Morristown, New Jersey 07960. (201) 538-0700.] Open May–Oct. Area 2.*

Elms Farm Inn, New York

New York

Anyone who has not been beyond the urban areas in New York State has missed a scenic countryside with more than 8,000 lakes, rugged mountains, island-dotted rivers, rock-faced glens and villages where houses of colonial days stand as reminders of the pioneering past. Control of the land was in the hands of the Dutch, the French, the powerful Iroquois Nation or the English until the Revolutionary War, followed by statehood in 1788. It's a state of farmlands, orchards and vineyards, and in the mountains are 42 peaks that rise 4,000 feet or more.

ALL BREEZE GUEST FARM invites you to "enjoy country fresh air, organic vegetables, a spring-fed pond and tasty family-style meals" on a peaceful and informal 35-acre farm. You'll stay with Joan Manning and her three sons (12, 16, and 17) in their home or in the guest house. The farmhouse dining-room is a favorite gathering-spot. There are lawn games and a pond. "The Mannings' farm is an ideal place for a restful vacation," writes a visitor. "The family-style meals are good, the hosts are congenial and the countryside is beautiful."

☐ Accom. 20 guests in family-sized rooms w./pvt. baths. Weekly AP: A $126, C to 9 yrs., $65. Daily AP: A $18, C $9. 100 mi. NW of NYC. From Port Jervis—go W on Rt. 97, right at rd. marked Hillside, up hill & left to farm (2½ mi.). Meet bus in Barryville, no chg. *Joan Manning, All Breeze Guest Farm, Barryville, New York 12719. Tel.: (914) 557-6167. Open Jul. & Aug., weekends all year. Area 2.*

BOGGS' RIVERSIDE overlooks the Hudson River from the Adirondack foothills. "The Boggs are wonderful hosts," writes a guest. "We fished from their dock, rowed their boat, explored their farm. It was carefree fun, comfortable, refreshing." Hosts no longer farm their 400 acres but do keep a vegetable garden from which you may help yourself. Swim at a sandy beach, hike, fish, picnic and relax. Horseback riding and square dances nearby.

☐ Accom. 20 guests in 2 dbls. in farmhouse, 2 rustic housekeeping cabins & 1 apt., pvt. & shared baths. Weekly EP: $55–$85/unit. Trailer parking $4.50/day. 200 mi. N of NYC; 1 mi. N of Corinth at carwash. *Donald & Winona Boggs, Boggs' Riverside, River Road., Corinth, New York 12822. Tel.: (518) 654-9216. Open all year. Area 5.*

ELMS FARM INN features a gracious, century-old farmhouse in a picturesque valley overlooking a trout-stocked pond and brook. It's a working dairy farm with chickens, goats, sheep, rabbits and ducks. "We all loved it," exclaims a guest. "It far exceeded all our expectations. For the first time all our children independently found ways to amuse themselves." Lots to choose from: tennis, swimming pool, evening hayrides or square dances, scenic hiking trails in 1,000 acres of woods and meadows, barbecues and rec room. Cooperstown and Howe Caverns nearby, if you can tear the family away long enough to visit them. Delicious family-style meals.

☐ Accom. for 45 guests. Weekly AP: A $110–$150, C $50–$90, pvt. family bath $35 addl. Also daily rates. 150 mi. NW of NYC—take NY Thruway to exit 19, N on Rt. 28 to Bovina Center sign past Andes, right & follow farm signs. Meet plane in Oneonta, $10/carload, bus in Lake Delaware, no chg. *Anthony & Dorothy Fratantoni, The Elms Farm, Bovina Center, New York 13740. Tel.: (607) 832-4340. Open all year. Area 8.*

FAR VIEW FARM is a working dairy farm with a free stall milking parlor on 265 acres. "We serve homemade breads, our own meat, and fresh vegetables from the garden," say the Meads. Their boys are 11 and 14, and young guests will make good use of the hayloft, play area, sandpile, swing and games—and there's archery, hiking, biking and fishing, if watching farm activities doesn't take up all your time. "I liked it because I could do what I wanted, when I wanted—just rest and ramble around," writes a guest. Trees, flowerbeds and lawns (with a small stream) surround the centrally air-conditioned farmhouse. Piano, if you play, or bring your own instrument. Boatlaunch, beaches, stables, Remington and Antique Boat Museums nearby; day trips to Lake Placid and Eisenhower Locks (3 hrs.), 1,000 Islands (45 min.). X-country skiing in winter. House rule is, "No smoking, no drinking."

☐ Sgls. & dbls. in farmhouse, shared bath, for 6–8 guests. Daily AP: A $20, C $12, under 2 yrs. free. 65 mi. N of Syracuse—go N on I-81 to Adams, W on Hwy. 178 to 2nd light, straight onto Smith Rd., 1st farm on left. Meet plane/bus in Watertown, or bus in Adams, $5/person or $10/carload. *Larry & Judith Mead, Far View Farm, Star Rt., Adams, New York 13605. Tel.: (315) 938-5441. Open all year. Area 1.*

FIELDSTONE FARM is a spot to relax and enjoy the scenery, or visit the Cooperstown museums—you can tailor your own vacation. "We enjoy it," writes a guest, "because the whole family participates together. The scenery's quiet and beautiful, the hosts extremely hospitable, the other guests cordial." The Burdts have 3 children (11 to 17) and there's lots for kids to do on this 200-acre semi-active farm with its hay crop for the riding horses. Well-equipped playground, large lawns, heated pool, new tennis court and recreation hall. Hayride-and-barbecue a popular new feature, and the area is good for auctions, antiques, boating, fishing and golf. "Honor system" grocery store on the property.

☐ Accom. 70 guests in 5 housekeeping apts. & 5 cabins, each w./pvt. bath, 1–3 bedrooms, living room/dining room, kitchen. Weekly EP: $145–$225 for 4-8, $20 ea. addl. Riding incl. 190 mi. NW of NYC—take NY Thruway to exit 21, W on Rt. 23, N on Rt. 145, W on US 20, W on Rt. 80 to Springfield Center or Cooperstown, phone for directions. Meet plane in Oneonta or train in Utica, $15/carload; bus in Cooperstown, no chg. *Herb & Dylis Burdt, Fieldstone Farm, R.D. 3, Box 118Z, Richfield Springs, New York 13439. Tel.: (315) 858-0295. Open all year. Area 4.*

GARNET HILL LODGE, overlooking pristine Thirteenth Lake where deer feed at the water's edge, lies within the New York State Forest Preserve—the largest wild forest area east of the Mississippi. Its 600 acres give novice or experienced hikers quick access to primitive settings here and in other parts of the Adirondack Park. Canoeing or tubing on the Hudson River is another favorite activity, or a day trip to the ice caves of Chimney Mountain. "People come here for a change of pace," the Heims tell us, "—to look at the mountains, watch the sunset, see the stars." Activities that vary with the season include swimming, sailing, tennis, exploring Garnet Mine, searching for old bottles, fishing, tapping the maple trees and boiling the syrup, snowshoeing, ice skating, tobogganing and x-country skiing. Excellent dining in the rustic lodge.

☐ Accom. up to 85 guests in lodges and chalets, pvt. & shared baths. Weekly MAP: dbl. $120, sgl. $140, addl. person in room $90–$100. Also daily, group & family rates & vacation home rentals. From New York City, 4½-hour drive—I-87 to exit 23, Rts. 9 & 28 to North River, left at sign. Meet bus in North Creek, $5/person, or Warrensburg, $10. *George & Mary Heim, Garnet Hill Lodge, North River, New York 12856. Tel.: (518) 257-2827. Open all year. Area 2.*

GLEN DURHAM, nestled in the Catskills, specializes in well-trained horses, lessons, and trail riding on 154 secluded acres. The hosts emphasize "quiet country lodging, old-fashioned hospitality and fine food" at their "charming colonial house." "It's delightfully rustic," writes a guest, "off the beaten path." The sugar house produces maple syrup in late February and March, and harvesting wildflower honey comes with the fall. Hook into trout in stocked ponds, hike the farm and nearby state trails. Near Catskill Mountains activities and five ski areas, Game Farm and auctions. Tack and gift shop on premises. Non-smokers, non-drinkers preferred.

☐ Accom. 6 guests, shared bath. Weekly AP: A $250 w./riding & instruction, $150 without, (or $40 & $25 daily). C under 8 yrs., 50% less. 135 mi. N of NYC—take NY Thruway exit 21, Rt. 23 W to South Durham, turn right, next right on Morrison Rd. about 1½ mi. Meet train in Hudson, $10/carload, bus in Cairo or Catskill, no chg. *David & Janice Nascimbeni, Glen Durham, Sunside-Cairo, New York 12413. Tel.: (518) 622-9878. Open all year. Area 8.*

GOLDEN ACRES FARM RESORT combines down-on-the-farm life with modern resort comforts. Children get to feed the animals, milk a cow and collect eggs on this 400-acre farm. Supervised day camp for 1- to 12-year-olds, teen program, organized adult activities. Bonfires, hayrides, boating and fishing, free pony and horseback riding with instruction. Heated outdoor pool, day and night tennis courts, basketball and handball courts, square and folk dancing, entertainment nightly. Single parents with children welcome. Farm camp for 10- to 16-year-olds without parents. Food from the farm, good home baking, snack bar. Jewish Dietary Laws observed. Central to six ski centers, Howe Caverns, Cooperstown, auctions, fairs, golf.

Golden Acres Farm Resort, New York

☐ Accom. 250 guests in motel/lodge-type units. Weekly MAP: A $140–$200. Weekly AP: C $90–$150. Riding incl. Also "you-cook" apts. EP rates, 4-day midweek & 3-day weekend pkg. rates. 145 mi. NW of NYC—take NY Thruway to exit 21, W on Rt. 23 for 40 mi. to Grand Gorge, sharp right at light onto Rt. 30, 2½ mi. to sign, left 2 mi. Meet bus in Grand Gorge, no chg. *Jerry & Anita Buxbaum, Golden Acres Farm & Ranch, R.D. 3, Gilboa, New York 12076. Tel.: (212) 246-9333 or (607) 588-7329. Open all year. Area 8.*

HARTELIUS COTTAGES are "attractive, clean and neat with big airy rooms," writes Mr. Hartelius, whose family has lived on this Catskill Mountain property since 1800. It's a 240-acre farm growing organic garden vegetables—also sheep, cows, goats, ducks and chickens. "We've spent many happy summers here," recalls a guest. "It's a beautiful setting, everything well kept, terrific swimming pool, and the recreation barn is a draw for young or old." Lawn games, and fertile ground for guests to do some gardening. Crafts a specialty, along with old-time movies. Children love the wading creek and acres of playground. Woodstock arts and crafts colony nearby; summer theater, Minnewaska State Park, ice caves, game farm, antiques and auctions.

☐ Accom. 30 guests in 10 cottages for 3–6 w./living room, kitchen, pvt. bath. Weekly EP: $90–$110 for 3, $10/ea. addl. Linens extra. 90 mi. N of NYC—go N on US 287 to exit 18, W on Rts. 299 & 44, N on Rt. 209 to Kerhonkson, N on Samsonville Rd. past laundromat, left up hill. Meet bus in Kerhonkson, no chg. *The Hartelius Family, Hartelius Cottages, Box 892, Cherrytown Rd., Kerhonkson, New York 12446. Tel.: (914) 626-5297 or 2876. Open all year. Area 8.*

HOLIDAY ACRES is open for adults only "to stay in our lovely old Colonial house," Sherry writes, "and to enjoy a change of pace on our peaceful 400-acre dairy farm on the scenic Unadilla River." They relax in the 20- by 40-foot heated swimming pool and under shade trees on the spacious lawn, or row the boat on the farm pond. For a look at museums, antiques shops, flea markets, fairs and auctions they drive to Cooperstown or other historic points. Also golf, bowling, square dances and summer theater.

□ Accom. 8 adults in sgl. & dbl. rooms, 2 baths. Weekly AP, $115; MAP, $100. 225 mi. NW of New York City—N on Thruway to exit 30, S on Rt. 51 & W on US 20 to West Winfield, left 1½ mi. at light, right 1½ mi. at Fork Rd. Meet plane/train/bus in Utica, $10/carload. *Carlton & Sherry Wilcox, Holiday Acres, Rt. 1, Box 240, West Winfield, New York 13491. Tel.: (315) 822-6028. Open Jun.–Sep. Area 4.*

LITTLE TEXAS RANCH, 500 acres in the Catskill Mountains, is noted for lots of horseback riding at very reasonable rates. Wranglers guide you on short rides, all-day rides and overnight pack trips, and give riding instruction. "It's really for riders, not for others," guests say. Things are old-fashioned and rustic, and when you're not riding you can pitch in with haying or caring for the horses, go on hayrides, fish in the pond, play games or watch a movie in the rec room, and the Long Horn Saloon is really hopping on Saturday nights. It's a half-hour drive to tennis and swimming, but a new pool and courts are in the plans. The public as well as guests use the General Store and cocktail lounge. Snowmobiling, ice skating, sledding and x-country skiing in winter.

□ Accom. 60 guests. Hotel rooms for 30, weekly AP, dbl. occup.: $107 sharing bath, $125 w./pvt. bath, riding incl. Sgl., triple, daily & winter weekend rates available. Also housekeeping units for 30, next to horse barn (not for everyone), $400/season EP, riding extra. 120 mi. NW of New York City— Rt. 17 to Roscoe, W at traffic light, cross bridge, right & follow signs 9 mi. Meet plane in Monticello, $5/person; bus in Roscoe, no chg. *James & Rita Greier, Little Texas Ranch, Box 36, Obernburg, New York 12767. Tel.: (914) 482-5759. Open all year. Area 7.*

MERRILL'S FARM is on 450 acres at the edge of the Catskill Forest Preserve near Beaverkill River. "Great for a family with young children," as one guest put it. Everyone likes to try milking a cow—and there are pigs to feed, eggs to gather, frogs to catch. You can hike, fish, swim, go canoeing. Golfing, bowling, movies, antiques, Farmers' Museum and Howe Caverns close at hand. In winter, there's skiing, skating, tobogganing, and snowmobiling. Games and goodies in the rec room, home-grown vegetables at meals, and Mrs. Merrill whips up cinnamon buns and pastry—"simple and plentiful," she says.

☐ 5 dbls. & 2 sgls. in guest house, shared baths, for 14 guests. Weekly AP: A $105–$115, C $75–$80. Also weekend rates. 120 mi. N of NYC, 12 mi NW of Roscoe. Take NY Thruway exit 16, W on Rt. 17 to Horton exit 92, right, then right on Horton Brook Rd. Meet bus in Roscoe, no chg. *John & Vivian Merrill, Merrill's Farm, R.D. 1, Roscoe, New York 12776. Tel.: (607) 498-4212. Open all year. Area 8.*

MERWIN'S FISHING PRESERVE is an angler's dream, with nine stocked spring-fed ponds on its rolling 52 acres. There's never a closed season, and no license is required for hooking the brown and rainbow trout, large and small mouth bass, perch, bull heads, strawberry bass and blue gills. There are outdoor fireplaces, picnic tables and play areas with swimming and rowboats. Guests are welcome at a nearby country club, and some attend the Berkshire Music Festival, 20 miles away. In

Little Texas Ranch, New York

winter they come for ice fishing, snowmobiling, x-country skiing and skating. The fourth generation of Merwins now lives in the 150-year-old remodeled homestead. They bake a loaf of bread for you when you arrive.

☐ Accom. 3 families, main house & apts., pvt. baths, kitchens. Weekly EP, $150/family, or daily $25. Less Dec.–Mar. 150 mi. N of New York City—144 mi. N on Taconic Parkway, exit on Rt. 203 for 5½ mi., right ¾ mi. on Merwin Rd. Meet plane/bus in Albany, train in Hudson, reas. chg. *Paul, Jane & Louise Merwin, Merwin's Fishing Preserve, R.F.D. 2, Box 127, Valatie, New York 12184. Tel.: (518) 392-9083 or 9065. Open all year. Area 8.*

MOUNTAINBROOK CHALET is secluded in the greenery of a Catskill hillside where the air's fresh and the brook bubbles. "I love this place and the picturesque area," a guest informs us. "The units are well-furnished. I love the delicious cooking, clean swimming pool, and the charming Mrs. Wolf." You can fish, hike, ride, play golf, dance and hunt bargains at auctions. Enjoy the peace and relaxation of the cozy fireplace and games at the chalet. There are swings, slides and lawn games for tots and some farm activities and animals to watch. No passing traffic, just right for a casual holiday. Chalet food is German-American. Near Howe Caverns, Cooperstown and other interesting places.

☐ Accom. 35–40 guests in 2-room housekeeping apts., also farmhouse w./2 bedrooms. Weekly EP: $115 for 2, $15 ea. addl. Weekly MAP: $108, C less. Also daily rates. 170 mi. N of NYC—take NY Thruway to exit 19, N on Rt. 28 for 65 mi. to 5 mi. beyond Andes, right to Bovina Center & 3 mi. beyond. Meet bus in Lake Delaware or Bovina Center Corner, no chg. *Mrs. Anna Wolf, Mountainbrook Chalet, Bovina Center, New York 13740. Tel.: (607) 832-4424. Open all year. Area 8.*

POLSTER'S FARM RESORT offers New Yorkers a homey haven in its big, old-fashioned, yellow farmhouse and annex on 83 acres of Catskill dairy country. "Tessie," who loves people and enjoys their company, has been having guests here for 50 years! "We serve the best of delicious home cooking and baking and pride ourselves on cleanliness," she emphasizes. It's a family operation. Her daughter is now the hostess, and grandchildren 12 and 13 help, too. There's a filtered swimming pool, ping pong, horseshoes, sing-alongs with accordion music, fortune telling, bingo and other games.

☐ Accom. 30 guests in main house & annex, 4 shared baths, running water in each room. Weekly AP: A $105, C 50% less. Daily, $20/person. 110 mi. NW of New York City—N on Thruway to exit 16, Quickway (Rt. 17) to Liberty, W 12 mi. on Rt. 82, 3 mi. N of Jeffersonville. Meet plane in White Lake, bus in Liberty or Fosterdale, no chg. *Theresa Polster & Frances Elias, Polster's Farm Resort, R.F.D. 1, Callicoon, New York 12723. Tel.: (914) 482-4335. Open May–Oct. Area 7.*

ROCKING HORSE RANCH is a complete dude ranch on 1,000 acres of fields and hills with indoor and outdoor swimming pools. English and western riding, water skiing on the lake and snow skiing on the slopes—all sports for all seasons. "Very casual," reports a guest, "where everyone is your friend. Food and accomodations excellent. Plenty to do, especially for young adults and children." Hayrides, buggy rides, cocktail parties, bands, shows, square dancing, movies, saunas, cycling and games add to the fun. Specially for children is a ranching world of their own—goats, ducks, sheep, donkeys and llamas in the kiddies' animal farm. If that's not enough, visit the interesting historic sites of the area.

☐ Dbls. & family rooms in lodge & luxury units for 350–400 guests. Weekly MAP: A $215–$250, C $99–$109 (to 4 yrs. free). Riding incl. Also weekend & off-season rates. 75 mi. N of NYC—take NY Thruway to exit 18, E for 6 mi. (follow signs). Meet plane in Wallkill, train in Poughkeepsie, or bus in New Paltz, $6/carload. *The Turk Family, Rocking Horse Ranch, Box 306-FV, Highland, New York 12528. Tel.: (212) 925-3385 or (914) 691-2927. Open all year. Area 8.*

ROUNDUP RANCH offers an endless variety of sports on its scenic mountain acres. A large stable of fine horses provides the right mount for each rider, and trails wind through woodlands or across open fields. There are all-day rides and cookouts, and Saturday night rodeos in the huge indoor arena (open also on rainy days for riding). A nine-hole golf course surrounds the ranch buildings, and there are indoor and outdoor pools and saunas. Hikes, surrey rides, softball, badminton and other games are part of the day-to-day scene, as are excellent family-style meals, socializing in front of the fire or at the bar, and enjoying the evening entertainment. Vacationers speak of "great food, excellent riding, a friendly and helpful staff and very clean rooms" that have been drawing them back here for years.

☐ Accom. 100 guests in log cabins, motel units & main house,

Timberlock,
New York

Glen Durham,
New York

Roundup Ranch, New York

nearly all pvt. baths. Approx. $45/day/person AP; less 10%
6–11 yrs., 50% 3–5 yrs.; 1–2 yrs. free. Also weekend & mid-week
rates for 2–5 nights; riding & golf pkgs. 125 mi. NW of New
York City—N on Thruway to exit 16, W on Rt. 17 to exit 94, left
thru Roscoe & 10 mi. on Rd. 7 to Pepacton Reservoir, left on Rt.
30 to Downsville, 3 mi. N on Rt. 206. Meet bus in Roscoe,
$8/carload. *Mrs. Loni Markert, Roundup Ranch, Box H,
Downsville, New York 13755. Tel.: (607) 363-7300. Open all
year. Area 7.*

TIMBERLOCK, in the Adirondack Forest Preserve Wilderness,
is on beautiful Indian Lake, 15 miles long. "Your rustic cabin is
right on the lakeshore," the Catlins explain, "lighted by old-
time kerosene and gas lamps." Water is from mountain springs,
and cooking and refrigeration powered by bottled gas. "We
claim we go to Timberlock for the children's sake, but with
tennis, hiking, swimming, canoeing, flights in the seaplane,
freedom from the kitchen and phone, and the rich smell of the
woods surrounding us—I'm not sure!" one guest admits.
Abundant wildlife, birds, wildflowers, mountains to climb,
caves and mines to explore. Hearty farm-style meals, island
cookouts, chicken barbecues. Non-smokers preferred.
  □ Cabins, most w./pvt. bath, for 65 guests. Weekly AP: A
$161–$196, C $56–$140. Riding extra. 265 mi. N of NYC—take
NY Thruway to exit 24 at Albany, I-87 (Northway) to exit 23 at
Warrensburg, Rts. 9 & 28 N to Indian Lake, 10 mi. S on Rt. 30.
Meet bus in Indian Lake, $3/person. *Dick & Barb Catlin,
Timberlock, Sabael, Indian Lake, New York 12864. Tel.: (518)
648-5494. [Winter: Sugar Hill Farm, Rt. 2, Woodstock, Ver-
mont 05091. (802) 457-1621.] Open Jun.-Aug. Area 2.*

WHEATHILL HOLSTEIN. Fishermen have hauled 6- and 7-
pound large-mouth bass from the lake on this 1,500-acre dairy
farm. "Each cottage is private," writes a frequent guest, "the
fishing is fantastic, the lake is right on the lawn with your own
private boat, and the scenery is gorgeous. For the money it can't
be beat." You and the kids can swim and hike, of course, and
see the farm in operation. Enjoy nature and wildlife or hop over
to the Town Recreation Area (3 minutes away) for waterskiing,
speedboating, sailing, a drive-in theater and golf. Near
Cooperstown, the famed Farmers Museum, Baseball Hall of
Fame, Howe Caverns and country auctions.
  □ Accom. 25 guests in 3 housekeeping cottages for up to 6,
$110/week/unit EP; or new chateau for 7, $160/week. All

w./kitchens & pvt. baths. Weekend rates (except Jul.–Aug.). 180 mi. NW of NYC—take NY Thruway to Rt. 17, W to Roscoe exit, N to Downsville, Walton, Sidney Center. *Robert & Edna Pomeroy, Wheathill Holstein, Easy St., Box 367, Sidney Center, New York 13839. Tel.: (607) 369-7597. Open May–Nov. Area 7.*

WILLOW SIDE is casual and rural—a former dairy farm on a secluded island in the Thousand Islands area. There are ponies, cows, ducks, chickens and pets, and children usually take on some of the farm chores. Also fishing, swimming and boating—and if you don't bring your own you can use the Seamans' outboard (for a small charge). A sandy beach is nearby. "They're just great people," comments a guest. "They showed us around and my kids rode a pony. Best vacation we've had."

☐ Accom. 2 families in 2 mobile homes. Weekly EP: $85/unit for up to 6, $10 each addl. 50 mi. N of Syracuse—go N on I-81 to Rt. 193 to Ellisborg, N to Woodville, W on country rd., 2nd farm. *Robert & Ethel Seamans, Willow Side, Box 112, Woodville, New York 13698. Tel.: (315) 846-5496. Open Jun.–Sep. Area 1.*

North Carolina

The mystery of the lost colony, founded by Sir Walter Raleigh on Roanoke Island in 1587 after the French and Spanish had withdrawn, remains unsolved to this day. But the colony is remembered as the birthplace of Virginia Dare, the first child of English parentage to be born in America. Future colonists were the first to vote for complete separation from Britain, and North Carolina is one of the thirteen original colonies. Hundreds of places and events— the poignant historical drama of the Cherokees, homes of colonial times, churches, museums, plantations, forts and colorful gardens—add to the travel pleasure in this beautiful state.

CATALOOCHEE RANCH, high in the Smokies at 5,000 feet, adjoins Great Smoky National Park. This beautiful ranch, celebrating its 40th anniversary, offers no planned activities but you'll still find plenty to do. Ride, swim, hike, play tennis, or lawn games, trout fish or loaf. "It's our second home," enthuses a visitor, "an easy, happy place. Congenial guests—some from abroad—and such a variety of enjoyment. Spectacular scenery and good food." Nearby you'll discover whitewater trips and the Cherokee Indian Reservation.

☐ Accom. 40 guests in ranch house rooms & 5 family cabins, pvt. & shared baths. Daily AP: $24–$45. Family rates. Riding extra. 40 mi. W of Asheville—take I-40 W to Maggie exit, US 19 W 10 mi. to signs, 3 mi. up mtn. Meet plane in Asheville, $25/carload, bus in Waynesville, $8. *Cataloochee Ranch—ask for Alice Aumen, Rt. 1, Box 500-B, Maggie, North Carolina 28751. Tel.: (704) 926-1401. [Dec.–mid-Mar.: (704) 926-0285.[Open May–Oct. Area 1.*

Cataloochee Ranch, North Carolina

FOLKESTONE LODGE, small, secluded, old-fashioned and furnished with antiques, is right next to Great Smoky National Park. The park is an area for nature lovers, with miles of hiking trails past waterfalls and trout streams, and biking paths closed to auto traffic. "The Kranichs, a happy young couple, love the outdoors and share their knowledge of it enthusiastically," comments a guest. They can pack box lunches and take guests tubing down Deep Creek or on nature walks. They maintain a mountain lore library at the Lodge and have bicycle rentals. "We don't have any television," they explain, "but offer a recreational experience that will long be remembered." Also in the area are a Cherokee Indian Reservation and weekly auctions.

☐ Accom. 11 guests. A $22 for 2, $19 sgl., C $7, daily incl. breakfast. 60 mi. W of Asheville. From Bryson City follow signs to Deep Creek Campground to Lodge sign ¼ mi. from park gate. Meet plane/bus in Bryson City, no chg. *Bob & Irene Kranich, Folkestone Lodge, Rt. 1, Box 310, W. Deep Creek Rd., Bryson City, North Carolina 28713. Tel.: (704) 488-2730. Open Jun. thru Oct. Area 1.*

LULLWATER INN, in the Smoky Mountains, gets its name from Sugarfork Creek which tumbles through the property. Tall hemlocks, spruce, white pine and fruit trees surround and shade Lullwater. After a breakfast of buttermilk biscuits and fresh eggs, why not climb the mountain up to the waterfall? Or go fishing, swimming or tubing downriver. An hour's drive takes you to Fontana Dam or the Cherokee Indian Reservation, and it's an interesting half-day trip to Smoky Mountain National Park or the Biltmore Estate in Asheville. The Smiths have children (9 and 10), so there are plenty of games and an occasional hayride. Excellent dinners—vegetables fresh from the organic garden. No alcohol, smoking outdoors only. Church groups can be accommodated.

☐ Inn rooms, weekly: MAP, A $105, 4-18 yrs. $15-$90; EP $100/room. Housekeeping units, weekly: $150/unit EP. Campsites weekly: $30-$42. Also daily rates. Accom. 30 guests. 75 mi. W of Asheville, 7 mi. E of Franklin on US 64. *Bob & Virginia Smith, Lullwater Inn, Rt. 5, Box 540, Franklin, North Carolina 28734. Tel.: (704) 524-6532. Open Apr. thru Nov. Area 1.*

PISGAH VIEW RANCH, 2,000 acres next to Pisgah National Forest and Smoky Mountain National Park, has miles of riding and hiking trails, a swimming pool, tennis court, wading and boating ponds, pioneer museum and gift shop. "We've never found a friendlier place," comments a family that goes back every year. "The food is great, rooms clean and the scenery just beautiful." You can make cider, pitch hay, join in evening square dancing and talent nights, visit the nearby farmers' market or attend a painting workshop. "We have guests from around the world—and even from far-away Brooklyn," Ruby comments. Non-drinking guests preferred.

☐ Modern cottages w./pvt. baths for 100 guests. Weekly AP: $125-$175; daily, $25-$33; less for 3rd in room. Riding extra. 18 mi. SW of Asheville—go 7 mi. W on US 19, S on Rt. 151 to 6 mi. past Candler to sign. Meet plane or bus in Asheville, $6-$8/carload. *Chester & Ruby Cogburn, Pisgah View Ranch, Rt. 1, Candler, North Carolina 28715. Tel.: (704) 667-9100. Open May–Dec. Area 1.*

SPRINGDALE LODGE is just off the Blue Ridge Parkway and "ideal for people who want to relax in the mountains," the Tingles explain. "The scenery is spectacular, and we are near wilderness trails in Pisgah National Forest. For those who want activity we have tennis and golf." The Lodge, in fact, is next to a golf course—"a true test for the low-handicap golfer"—where there's a dining room for family-style dinners, and a snack shop. You can fish or swim in Pigeon River, visit Great Smoky National Park and the Cherokee Indian Reservation, and in season pick fruits and vegetables at local farms.

☐ Lodge rooms & new log cabins, all w./kitchenettes & pvt. baths, accom. 22 guests. Weekly EP: room, $62.50/person, C 50% less; cabin, $200 for 4. Also daily & monthly rates. 30 mi. SW of Asheville. 11 mi. S of Waynesville on US 276. Meet plane in Asheville, $35/trip or $10/person. *Fred & Eunice Tingle, Springdale Lodge, Rt. 2, Box 197, Canton, North Carolina 28716. Tel.: (704) 235-8451. Open Apr.–Oct. Area 1.*

North Dakota

Prairies of waving grain stretch for endless miles in the east central part of the state, with neither tree nor hill to intercept the low horizon and big, big sky. The topography changes to the west where the grotesquely eroded Badlands begin, and the Missouri River flows. A 70,436-acre park of scenic splendor commemorates Teddy Roosevelt's conservation activities here. After explorations by the French and Spanish, and later by Lewis and Clark, in this land of long prairies, plateaus, buttes, conical hills and petrified forests, the state became settled and joined the Union in 1889.

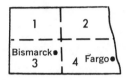

HANSEN FAMILY FARM is a 2,500-acre working ranch with a feedlot for 1,000–2,000 calves, a cow-calf operation, and circle irrigation systems for corn, alfalfa and grain. It's family-operated—with five Hansen children 6 to 13. Ride horses or join in farm activities that vary with the seasons. "We welcome everyone, especially foreign guests who wish to see a true picture of American agriculture," Nancy tells us. They have come from as far as Japan, Brazil and Australia. Nearby activities include auctions and square dancing.

☐ Accom. 7 guests in 2 dbls. & family room in farmhouse, shared baths. Daily AP: A $18, C $15, incl. riding. 120 mi. SW of Fargo. From Aberdeen (SD)—N on US 281 to Ellendale, E on Rt. 11 to Ludden, N to Oakes, 7 mi. S & 3 mi. E to farm. Meet plane/train/bus in Aberdeen, $15 carload. *Larry & Nancy Hansen, Hansen Family Farm, Rt. 2, Oakes, North Dakota 58474. Tel. : (701) 783-4410. Open Mar.–Nov. Area 4.*

Ohio

As far back as 800 B.C. the culture of the ancient Mound-builders flourished in what is now Ohio. They raised crops, traded and created unique effigy mounds which today may be seen in many parts of the state. It was after the American Revolution that the British ceded their right to Ohio and soon after, in 1803, it gained statehood. Half the land is fertile prairie on which dairy herds and crops are raised. The Amish area around Sugarcreek produces vast amounts of Swiss cheese, and from Van Wert comes the world's entire supply of Liederkranz. There is history to trace in every town and village.

CIRCLE K RANCH is a place for children to vacation without their parents, or where a family can stay in a cottage furnished with antiques. All the Kerns (three children in their 20s) operate the 200-acre farm with woods, a creek and a pond. They plant corn, soybeans, oats, hay and have 18 horses and ponies, and some calves, goats, chickens, 10 cats and 2 dogs. Trail rides every morning, and wiener roasts, hayrides and homemade ice cream. "We loved it so much that we've bought a farm of our own," writes a guest. "The Kerns are super people and you can quote me if you like," says another.

☐ Accom. 1 family in 6-room cottage w./bath; & 4 children (w/o parents) in farmhouse. Weekly AP: C $115. Cottage, weekly EP: A $35, C $25, min. $100. Riding incl. 30 mi. S of Columbus; 5 mi. S of Circleville, meet bus, no chg. *Cliff & Marjorie Kerns, Circle K Ranch, 26525 Gay-Dreisbach Rd., Circleville, Ohio 43113. Tel.: (614) 474-3711. Open May thru Oct. Area 8.*

McNUTT FARM provides "unlimited enjoyment" and lodging for outdoorsmen and families in the farmhouse or an outdoor sleeping deck, with a separate kitchen for guests to use. You can learn to milk "Hollyberry," feed horses and cattle, work at chores or read and relax—"Whatever is to your liking," says Don McNutt. It is especially a place to bring your own horse and ride to your heart's content. Trail and tour guide service available, plus instruction in backcountry horsemanship including advice on conditioning the horse for long distance riding, under saddle or in harness. Hike or ride to the Outpost for overnight camping. The farm adjoins the Blue Rock State Forest—a scenic preserve with beautiful wilderness trails, swimming, boating, fishing, a beach and nature programs. No drinking; non-smokers preferred.

□ Rooms in lodge-type farmhouse for 30 guests, shared baths. Daily EP: $10/person; trail guide service, $15 & up; horse lot, $2. Also group rates. 60 mi SE of Columbus, 11 mi S of Zanesville—go S on Rt. 60, follow Blue Rock State Forest signs to farm. Meet plane in Columbus, bus in Zanesville, reas. chg. *Don & Patty McNutt, McNutt Farm, 6120 Cutter Lake Rd., R. 1, Blue Rock, Ohio 43720. Tel.: (614) 674-4555. Open all year. Area 5.*

TWIN VALLEY FARM & CAMPGROUND means real summer fun if you're a youngster, and total relaxation if you're adult. There's a cinderblock cabin for non-campers, and for others 100 well-kept campsites. Kids can ride ponies, go on hayrides, play on swings, wade in the creek, fish or swim at the lake, watch the chickens, hogs, cows, mare and colt. "Best place in the world for kids," comments one guest. And the parents? "I never rested so much since I was born." All agree the Dunlaps are "two grand people."

□ Cabin w./2 bedrooms, living room, kitchen accom. 7; $85/week EP. Also 100 campsites w./complete facilities. 35 mi. SE of Canton; from Carrollton—4 mi. S on Rt. 43, 3 mi. E on rd. 27. *Lewis & Twila Dunlap, Twin Valley Farm & Campground, 2330 Apollo Rd. S.E., Carrollton, Ohio 44615. Tel.: (216) 739-2811. Open May thru Oct. Area 6.*

WALLACE'S WOODED ACRES is a quiet, friendly place to rest and enjoy nature—just right for families with small children. Guests live in a mobile home and two A-frames, but often sit on the porch and chat with the Wallaces who generously share produce from the garden as well as recipes. They raise beef cattle and crops, take guests on wagon rides, and arrange for the kids to visit neighbors to see farm animals. Nearby sights include covered bridges, historic Schoenbrunn Village, Piedmont and Tappan Lakes, glass factories and a coal mine tour.

☐ A-frames & 2-bedroom cabin, pvt. yards, fully furnished for 3 families. Weekly AP: $100/unit. 70 mi. W of Pittsburgh, 9 mi. E of Cadiz on US 22. *William & Olive Wallace, Wallace's Wooded Acres, R.D. 3, Cadiz, Ohio 43907. Tel.: (614) 968-4302. Open Jun.–Oct. Area 6.*

WINDY ACRES offers families with young children a chance to see a working farm in action. You'll stay in a trailer home next to the farmhouse while getting to know the cows, calves, sows, sheep, chickens, goats and rabbits. "The Johnsons are hard-working, very down-to-earth people," reports a guest. "We were more than pleased with our 'mini' holiday at a nominal price—a good, clean vacation both in atmosphere and accommodations." Plenty of Johnson grandchildren who live in the area will join you for wiener roasts, hayrides, lawn games & baseball. Non-drinking guests are preferred.

☐ Trailer home for up to 6 guests, $100/family/week EP. 200 mi. SW of Cleveland—take I-71, Rt. 37 & Hwy. 347 to E. Liberty, 2 mi. on Rd. 10 to Rd. 129, 2nd house on left. *Kenny & Nancy Johnson, Windy Acres, Rt. 1, Zanesville, Ohio 43360. Tel.: (513) 666-4741. Open Jun.–Sep. Area 4.*

McNutt Farm, Ohio

Oregon

Portland
Salem
Medford

Oregon's varied topography, with snow-capped mountains, streams, valleys, deserts, prairies, waterfalls, lakes and a magnificent coast, make it one of the most scenic states. In 1792 the U.S. claimed this territory, and in 1805 Lewis and Clark explored it. Next came fur trappers and the British, but the colonists decided in favor of the U.S., and in 1859 Oregon became a state. In the south is the famous Crater Lake, set in the center of a prehistoric volcano. The state is the home of hard-riding cowboys, and in September top rodeo performers and local Indians converge for four days of Old West pageantry and the rip-snortin' Pendleton Roundup.

BAR M RANCH dates back to 1864 when the log ranch house was built as a stagecoach stop. The magic word here is *horse*—one for each guest, instruction, unlimited riding and 1- or 2-day campouts. "We have elbow room and unseen values for the whole family," the Bakers report. You can round up strays and feed the horses, calves and pigs, play a game of tennis, fish for trout, watch deer and eagles. At the rec barn there's basketball, volleyball and square dancing. Or just relax and do nothing. "The Bakers are excellent hosts," comments a guest. "The food is superb, the atmosphere friendly and informal, and the natural warm springs pool mighty welcome after a long ride." The ranch is next to the Umatilla Indian Reservation.

☐ Accom. 35 guests in ranch house, annex & cabins, pvt. & shared baths. Weekly AP: A $175–$220, C (over 5 yrs. only) $165; incl. riding. Camp-out $7.50-$10. 31 mi. E of Pendelton—take Rt. 11, follow Thornhollow, Gibbon or Bar M markers;

Bar M Ranch, Oregon

cross UP tracks at Thornhollow, continue E to ranch. Meet plane/train/bus in Pendleton, bus in Walla Walla, $20/person. *Gene & Hope—Howard & Bonnie—Baker, Bar M Ranch, Rt. 1, Adams, Oregon 97810. Tel.: (503) 566-3381. Open Jun. thru Sep. Area 1.*

DONNA GILL'S ROCK SPRINGS GUEST RANCH is in the ponderosa pine country of central Oregon, next to the Deschutes National Forest. It's a beautiful setting for riding, fishing, tennis (two courts), volleyball, pony and hayrides and swimming in the heated pool. There are forty horses on the ranch, and riding and tennis clinics. "We used to go abroad," confesses one guest, "but our children have more freedom here and a marvelous time. A truly outstanding ranch, with really good food, great company, fine accommodations, and fun for all ages." In the evenings there's dancing, singing—someone pumps the player piano—cards and sitting around the fireplace. Many nearby attractions to enjoy, including horse shows, rodeos, golf and fishing streams and lakes.

☐ Accom. 40 guests in cottages complete w./sitting room, fireplace, kitchen, daily maid service. Weekly AP: about $330/person, incl. riding. Your babysitter accom. free. Off-season cottage rentals. 160 mi. SE of Portland. From Bend—take US 20 NW 6 mi. to Tumalo Emporium, turn left & follow signs 3 mi. to ranch. Meet plane in Redmond, bus in Bend, no chg. *Pancho Aramburu, Mgr., Donna Gill's Rock Springs Guest Ranch, 64201 Tyler Rd., Bend, Oregon 97701. Tel.: (503) 382-1957. Open all year. Area 5.*

GREEN SPRINGS BOX R RANCH, a cattle ranch in the Cascade Mountains, just two miles from the Pacific Crest Trail, spreads over meadow, timberland, and rock formations. There's a main house built in 1910 as a stagecoach stop, horse barn with

Green Springs Box R Ranch, Oregon

tack room, old blacksmith shop, boot hill, and two modern, rustic log houses with fireplaces for guests. It's a place to unwind and relax, or hike, fish, hunt arrowheads or spot wild animals. Anyone can join Ed with the chores—branding, irrigating, delivering calves, fixing fences or gathering firewood. "Best time for haying is August," he says, "May and October for branding, June for wildflowers and December to March for snow." No drinking; non-smokers preferred.

☐ Accom. 8-10 persons in ea. cabin, w./pvt. bath & washer-dryer. Weekly EP: $200/cabin; daily EP: $35. 23 mi. E of Ashland. From I-5 take Hwy. 66 exit, 90 E 23 mi., exit left on dirt rd. ¾ mi. *Ed & Grace Overstreet, Green Springs Box R Ranch, 16799 Hwy. 66, Ashland, Oregon 97520. Tel.: (503) 482-1873. Open all year. Area 7.*

HURTLEY QUARTER HORSE RANCH, in full view of seven snowcapped mountains, is where the Hurtleys breed, raise, race, show and sell quarter horses. "Guests may sit and gaze out across green pastures where horses graze," they suggest, "or they may roll up their sleeves and get into it with us." "Getting into it" can mean cleaning stalls and corrals, working with the horses, changing irrigation pipe and feeding. Or you can watch the foals (February through June is foaling season), swim in the pond or ride in the surrey. Kids can go dirt bike riding and exploring with the boys (12 and 8 years). "Plain ol' ranch cooking'," Judy says. Many things to see and do in this recreation area. The Hurtleys have snowmobiles; ski resort 20 miles away.

☐ Accom. 1 family at a time in ranch house or cabin. Daily AP: $30, C $20. Also EP rates; campsites and trailer hookups. 18 mi. W of Bend, 4 mi. E of Sisters on Hwy. 126. Meet plane/bus in Portland, Bend, Redmond or Sisters, reas. chg. *Dave & Judy Hurtley, Hurtley Quarter Horse Ranch, Star Route, Hwy. 126, Sisters, Oregon 97759. Tel.: (503) 548-3487. Open all year. Area 5.*

Landis Farm Guest Home, Pennsylvania

Pennsylvania

The Indians, Dutch, Swedes, Finns and the British are part of Pennsylvania's history—and so is Williman Penn. In 1680 the land was granted to him as a place where Quakers might have religious freedom. They soon were joined by the Mennonites, Amish, Dunkards and Moravians from Germany—called collectively the Pennsylvania Dutch. Today the quaint and colorful customs of the Plain People—decorative hex signs which are "chust for nice," bountiful cooking and folk festivals—delight the visitor. In this historic state the Continental Congress adopted the Declaration of Independence in 1776, and decisive battles of the Revolutionary and Civil Wars were fought.

BEAVER CREEK FARM CABINS are simple and well-furnished housekeeping units in the heart of Amish country on a farm raising 56,000 broiler chickens. "It's the best vacation we ever had," a guest tells us. "The Brubakers were terrific hosts as well as entertainers. Highlights included an unforgettable cave exploration, a hike along the Susquehanna River, homemade ice cream at the cookout and a hayride through the Amish farmlands." There are get-togethers every evening around the fire at the farm's pavilion. You may want to tour the quaint Pennsylvania Dutch countryside to Gettysburg, Hershey, Valley Forge, Molly Pitcher's home and French Creek. Brubaker children are 8, 12 and 17.

☐ Accom. 65 guests in 10 cabins w./pvt. bath, kitchen, living room, 1 or 2 bedrooms. Weekly EP: $125 for 2–4, $1.50/day ea. addl. 165 mi. SW of NYC, 9 mi. SE of Lancaster. Take PA Tpk. exits 21-23 to Strasburg, 1½ mi. S on Rt. 896. Meet plane/train/bus in Lancaster, $5/carload. *Harold & Miriam Brubaker, Beaver Creek Farm Cabins, Rt. 1, Strasburg, Pennsylvania 17579. Tel.: (717) 687-7745. Open Apr.–Jan. Area 9.*

CHESTNUT HILL RANCH is a friendly working guest ranch on 1,200 acres of "wonderful, wild wilderness of northern Potter County." The Fittings (sons 14, 16, 20) came here from Bucks County where Howard was an engineer and Jeanne a teacher. They raise sheep, goats and rabbits, grow hay and offer what one guest calls "the best riding I've ever had." It's western-style riding, with lessons, short and long trail rides and games on horseback on Saturday mornings. The "easygoing activities program" includes a swimming pool, badminton and other games, and taking in local carnivals, festivals and whitewater events. Well-stocked fishing streams are nearby. Cross-country skiing (rentals and groomed trails) in winter, and snowmobiling.

□ Accom. 16 guests in lodge and bungalow, mostly pvt. baths. AP, A: weekly $126–$158, daily $20–$25; C less; riding, $35/week, $7/day. Also MAP rates. 215 mi. NE of Pittsburgh, 300 mi. W of New York City. Take US 6 to Coudersport, N on Rt. 44 to Millport, E 2 mi. on Eleven Mile Rd., left 2 mi. on blacktop rd. Meet plane in Bradford, $12/carload; bus in Bolivar (New York), no chg. *Howard & Jeanne Fitting, Chestnut Hill Ranch, R.D. Box 77, Shinglehouse, Pennsylvania 16748. Tel.: (814) 698-3571. Open all year. Area 2.*

DYBERRY GLEN. When you're down on the farm with the Bassaks you're 1,400 feet up in the picturesque Moosic Mountains. Work begins before the rooster crows, but it's breakfast anytime for the guests. "We really go to eat, eat, eat, and sleep," confesses a family that returns each year. "Mrs. Bassak is a genius in the kitchen." She's famous for her Hungarian apple strudel (14 feet long in preparation), served every Sunday. Work up the necessary appetite any way you choose. Help drive the Holstein herd in from pasture, swim in the spring-fed pond, or head for nearby boating, golf, fishing, riding and hiking. Kids love the swings and sandbox, the Bassak twins (15) and their 10-year-old sister, the hayloft, and the cookie jar that's always open.

□ Accom. 12 guests in 6 dbls., pvt. baths. Weekly AP: A $125, C to 10 yrs., $60. 125 mi. NW of NYC. Take NY Thruway to Rt. 17, W to I-84, W to Rt. 6 to far end of Honesdale's Main St., Rt. 670 to Bethany, right at Wayne & Ash Sts., 2 mi. to

Dyberry Glen, Pennsylvania

farm. Meet bus in Honesdale, no chg. *The Bassak Family, Dyberry Glen, R.D. 3, Honesdale, Pennsylvania 18431. Tel.: (717) 253-1369. Open Apr.–Dec. Area 3.*

GRAN PINO FARMS is in a peaceful woodland setting, but the quiet is broken periodically when Henry bursts into Italian songs to a concertina accompaniment. The whole family (children 8, 12, 14) is musical, and Joanne is also into physical fitness, pacing off five miles of rolling countryside each morning—a change from the city sidewalks where they once lived. "We enjoy sharing the joy and good life we found here," they say. You can swim and go boating at their spring-fed lake, feed the animals, play volleyball or badminton, hike or fish, and in winter go ice skating, tobogganing and x-country skiing. Nearby there's golf, bowling, state parks and the Cowtown Rodeo in August. Homemade cakes, breads, pies and garden-fresh vegetables are on the table at mealtime.

◻ Accom. 1 family in large room w./bath. Daily AP: A $20, C $10. 55 mi. N of Pittsburgh—N 45 mi. on I-79, E on Rt. 108 thru Slippery Rock, 3 mi. on Rt. 8, right on Coaltown Rd., 1st farm on left. *Henry & Joanne Marino, Gran Pino Farms, R.D. 1, Boyers, Pennsylvania 16020. Tel.: (412) 794-6362. Open all year. Area 4.*

HILLSIDE FARM is a place "to get away from it all," as Carlene describes it. "You can relax, let the children run, help with the farm work, play volleyball and badminton, or visit Somerset County's attractions." These include antiques shops, craft shows, festivals and rafting the Youghiogheny. It's a 345-acre farm where the Schaeffers raise grain and a steer, chickens and hogs, and where their St. Bernards raise puppies. Leathercrafts and refinishing old tools are Jay's hobbies, and Carlene is up to giving lessons in macramé, crocheting and quilting. Their boys are three and four. Guests speak of "superlative food" including homemade ice cream. No drinking.

  □ Accom. 1 family, 2 bedrooms & bath. Daily AP: A $15, C $10; or $13 & $8 MAP. 60 mi. E of Pittsburgh. From Penn. Tpk. take exit 10, E on Rt. 31, N 6 mi. on Rt. 160, W toward Shanksville, right at 1st rd., 1st farm on left. Meet plane/train/bus in Somerset, $7/carload, or Johnstown, $20. *Jay & Carlene Schaeffer, Hillside Farm, R.D. 2, Friedens, Pennsylvania 15541. Tel.: (814) 267-5280. Open all year. Area 7.*

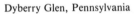

Dyberry Glen, Pennsylvania

HILLSTONE FARMS & CANYON TRAIL RIDES is in Pennsylvania's "Canyon Country." There's fun for the whole family on this 620-acre farm—ride horseback on scenic trails, go boating, milk a cow, pick corn, go fishing, hiking or on a hayride, and check up on the farm animals. "A very pleasant experience, terrific for kids. The hosts are magnificent people," writes a guest. "We sometimes see wild animals right from the front lawn," Mary Webster notes. Accommodations adequate, not fancy, with overflow area for campers. Swimming, golf, winter sports nearby. Riding and hayrides are for overnight guests only, not for campers.

   ☐ Accom. 1 or 2 families or group up to 12 in 4 dbl. rooms, pvt. & shared baths, living room & kitchen. Weekly EP: $280. Also daily rates, & rates for 1 or 2 dbl. rooms only w./pvt. bath. Riding extra. 250 mi. W of NYC, 5 mi. W of Wellsboro on Rts. 660 & 362. Meet plane in Corning or Williamsport, $20/carload; bus in Wellsboro or Mansfield, $5/carload. *Mrs. Mary Webster, Hillstone Farms & Canyon Trail Rides, R.D. 6, Box 298, Wellsboro, Pennsylvania 16901. Tel.: (717) 724-3184. Open all year. Area 2.*

THE INN AT STARLIGHT LAKE, open to guests since 1909, is a place they call "delightful, easy-going and hospitable." Here Jack & Judy (formerly in show business) have taken to innkeeping "as though they've done it all their lives." Tastefully renovated rooms retain the old inn flavor, and the congenial hosts provide an atmosphere of relaxation and conviviality—an excellent library of recorded music, live music and dancing at times, and wines, spirits and late night snacks. It's in the Moosic Mountains, an area of picturesque small towns, winding roads, forests, farmlands and pleasant activities for all seasons— swimming and boating at the Inn's spring-fed lake, tennis, biking, children's play area. Nearby: canoeing on the Delaware River, golf, ski slopes. 18 miles of marked x-country trails on the property.

   ☐ Accom. 60 guests in 30 dbl. rooms (some shared baths) & family suites. Weekly MAP: A, dbl. occup., $334–$360, C 7–16 yrs. $110, 1–7 yrs. no chg. Also daily, weekend, mid-week, holiday & ski rates. 180 mi. N of Philadelphia, 150 mi. NW of New York City—Rt. 17 N to Hancock, Rt. 191 S 2 mi. to Rt. 370, 3 mi. to Starlight, right 1 mi. Meet bus in Hancock (New York), no chg. *Jack & Judy McMahon, The Inn at Starlight Lake, Starlight, Pennsylvania 18461. Tel.: (717) 798-2519. Open all but Apr. Area 3.*

LAKE MOUNT FARM. The Young's motto, "forget your cares and leave the work to us," is easy to heed on this 165-acre mountain farm in Cherry Valley in the western Poconos. Wander along old logging and mining roads or hike the Appalachian trail. You'll see lush fields of grass and crops, and fish in a 12-acre lake for bass, pickerel, perch, bluegills and catfish. Swim in the pool, play tennis or go boating. "We've been coming here for years," says a guest. "The Pennsylvania Dutch food and the accommodations are satisfying, the hosts kind and hospitable." Golf, stables, bowling, outdoor movies nearby. In winter, ski at Camelback or toboggan on farm slopes and skate the pond. In spring children can see baby farm animals arrive— piglets, calves, chicks and kittens.

□ Cottages & motel units w./pvt. baths for 60 guests. Weekly AP: A $125, T $90, C $70. 90 mi. NW of NYC, 10 mi. S of Stroudsburg. From NYC take Rt. 22 to Rt. 33, N to Saylorsburg exit on new hwy., left at hotel, old Rt. 115. Meet bus in Saylorsburg, no chg. *Russell & Carrie Young, Lake Mount Farm, P.O. Box 66, Saylorsburg 2, Pennsylvania 18353. Tel.: (717) 992-4875. Open all year. Area 6.*

LOUJEAN ACRES provides a 7-room farmhouse for vacationing families, complete with kitchen. It's a working farm where the Fiskes (three children are 12, 16 and 20) raise Holstein dairy cattle, two pigs, ducks, chickens, rabbits, pony, dogs and cats. You can weed the garden, dig potatoes, swim, fish, hike, hunt fossils—or take it easy. "This type of vacation is perfect for me," concludes a guest. "It provides country surroundings, relaxation, a quiet atmosphere. I was allowed to milk a cow and use the family piano for practicing." If you're so lucky as to be there in the spring, you'll make maple syrup the old-fashioned way—or in fall gather apples for cider. Ski nearby in winter. A child 6 or over may live with the Fiskes.

□ Farmhouse for up to 13 guests. Weekly EP: $85/family. C 6 yrs. & up living w./Fiskes, weekly AP $85. Incl. linens. 165 mi. NW of NYC, 5 mi. N of Laceyville (on US 6). Meet plane in Avoca, train/bus in Scranton, bus in Laceyville, $10/carload. *Louis & Jeanne Fiske, Loujean Acres, Rt. 1, Box 258, Wyalusing, Pennsylvania 18853. Tel.: (717) 746-3306. Open all year. Area 3.*

LANDIS FARM GUEST HOME takes you back to Williamsburg of nearly 200 years ago. Its stone house for guests has been faithfully restored with the original walk-in fireplace, polished wide plank floor and shuttered door and windows. "It is heaven for the non-smoker and non-drinker," observes a guest, referring to the hosts' requirement. "We fell in love with it. The family is hard-working, like every Mennonite family, and the children (1, 5, 9, 11) are simply super." Work involves running a full dairy farm with a pipeline milking set-up, and you're invited to help or watch when you're not touring the Pennsylvania Dutch area.

☐ House w./2 bedrooms, living room, kitchen bath. EP: $140/week, $25/day, for 4; $10 or $5 each addl. 155 mi. SW of New York City, 60 mi. NW of Philadelphia. From Lancaster, W on Rt. 283, N on Rt. 722, left on Colebrook Rd., left on Gochlan Rd., 1st farm. *Earl & Evelyn Landis, Landis Farm Guest Home, R.D. 7, Manheim, Pennsylvania 17545. Tel.: (717) 898-7028. Open all year. Area 9.*

MAYFIELD occupies 80 acres in the uncrowded Cumberland Valley, with an 18th century farmstead on the Conodoguinet Creek which Shirley and Jerry are restoring with true authenticity. They are knowledgeable collectors of antiques, active in civic affairs, and eager to share their rural life with one family at a time who will plan their own activities. You can harvest and care for the kitchen garden and help with the crops and all the animals, or fish, hike, canoe or raft the creek in innertubes or cycle the winding road that follows it. It's a fascinating area with public auctions, antiques, crafts, fairs, swimming, tennis, golf, Amish farms and much history. Guests call Shirley "an excellent and generous cook." Eric, 12, shares in the hosting.

☐ Accom. family up to 6 in farm house or cottage, pvt. bath in each. Weekly MAP: A $110, C $55, under 2 yrs. free; daily A $20, C $10. 212 mi. W of New York City, 25 mi. W of Harrisburg. From I-81, take exit 12, N 2 mi. on Rt. 465 to Rt. 641, W 1.6 mi., N on McCallisters Rd., 1.7 mi. on Creek Rd. Meet plane/train/bus in Harrisburg, $5–$8/carload; bus in Carlisle, no chg. *Jerry & Shirley Hollowell, Mayfield, R.D. 9, Box 458, Carlisle, Pennsylvania 17013. Tel.: (717) 243-8944. Open May thru Sep. Area 8.*

ORCHARD ROCK COTTAGES in the Poconos—three housekeeping cottages—are in an apple orchard and surrounded by meadows, hillsides and woods. The primary crop is hay, with a small garden plot. "Total beauty, peacefulness, and friendly, helpful hosts" are guests' reactions to the 125 scenic acres with a tennis and basketball court, and five-minute walk down the lane

to a private, spring-fed lake with swimming, fishing, sailboat and rowboats. You'll socialize, play games, dance or read books in the large, converted barn evenings when you're not out enjoying the activities of this resort area. Wild deer roam the property. Guests may bring pets.

☐ Accom. 3 families. 2-bedroom units, $135/week EP; 3-bedroom unit, $170. 140 mi. W of New York City—Rts. 17 & 17B, then 7 mi. W on Rt. 371, right on paved rd., 4th house on left. *Peter & Philomena Niceforo, Orchard Rock Cottages, Star Route, Honesdale, Pennsylvania 18431. Tel.: (717) 224-6274. [Sep.-Jun.: 1109 Karen Terr., Linden, New Jersey 07036. (201) 381-0940.] Open Jul.-Aug. Area 3.*

POSEY PATCH ACRES, in the heart of Amish country, grows more than "poseys"—you'll find major crops of strawflowers and several greenhouses. The Weavers are interesting, chatty hosts who invite you to use their home as a base for touring this beautiful area—the Strasburg Railroad, Lancaster farm markets, flea market and Farmers Museum among points of interest. "We were completely delighted with each day at Posey Patch," says a guest. Your Mennonite hostess prepares good Pennsylvania Dutch-style food to satisfy the appetite you build up hiking, playing tennis, fishing in the creek or resting strenuously under the shade trees. The land deed goes back to William Penn.

☐ Dbl. & 2 family rooms, 2 baths, accom. 11 guests. Weekly AP: A $115, C $80. Also daily and EP rates. 160 mi. SW of NYC, 6 mi. E of Lancaster on Rt. 340. Meet plane/train/bus in Lancaster, $3/person. *Frank & Edith Weaver, Posey Patch Acres, Rt. 1, 2576 Old Philadelphia Pike, Bird-in-Hand, Pennsylvania 17505. Tel.: (717) 397-2111. Open all year. Area 9.*

QUALITY FIRST ACRES is an unusual 197-acre working farm where you can live in your own home away from home. Lots to see and do—50,000 laying hens, serenaded by continuous FM music, turn out 13 million eggs a year! 600 hogs and cattle. After you've had a look at the operation, head for the swimming pool and two-toned tennis court, the basketball court, the softball diamond, the pond for fishing and boating, the rec room or the riding stables. Playground for kids, hayrides for the young at heart. Golf and skiing nearby. The Trones have 5 children, from 10 to 23 years. "Loved the acres of open space," writes a visitor, "and the perfectly organized cottage. Our considerate and congenial hosts explained farm life to us. Outstanding!" Gettys-

Quality First Acres, Pennsylvania

burg, Lancaster, Hershey and York nearby; less than two hours from Washington, D.C.

☐ Accom. 50 guests in 2- & 3-bedroom cottages w./pvt. bath, living room w./convt. twin-bed sofa, kitchen, utensils, washer, color TV. Weekly EP: A $90, C–T $35; daily, A $15, C–T $7; off-season & group rates. 17 mi. E of Gettysburg—go E on Hwy. 30 to Abbottstown, N on Rt. 194 to East Berlin, ½ mi. N, cross bridge, left on Rife Rd. Meet plane in Hanover, bus in Abbottstown, no chg. *Tom & Jean Trone, Quality First Acres, Rife Rd., R.D. 2, East Berlin, Pennsylvania 17316. Tel.: (717) 259-0101 or 0102. Open all year. Area 8.*

ROSEBROOK COTTAGE is just the place for a budget-conscious family eager for a quiet, back-to-nature holiday—garden, outhouse and all. The cottage beside a stream, is fully equipped for housekeeping, with hot water, electricity and a newly installed shower. Ray built it, and his sister, Ruth, is a craftsman of doll furniture and miniatures (which have been televised). Any broken dolls? She restores and dresses them. "A nice little cottage, rustic but very clean," comments a neighbor. The area is full of carnivals, auctions, museums, church suppers and history. Some animals, fishing and swimming on the 5-acre farm. Non-drinkers preferred.

☐ Cottage for 1 family (7 beds), $75/week EP. 176 mi. NW of New York City. From Scranton, NW on Rt. 6 to Laceyville, 1 mi. on Rt. 367, 1st right turn, go 1 mi. Meet plane in Binghamton (New York), 12¢/mi.; bus in Laceyville, no chg. *Ray Inman, Rosebrook Cottage, R.D. 1, Box 119, Laceyville, Pennsylvania 18623. Tel.: (717) 869-1526. Open Apr.–Oct. Area 3.*

SILVER LAKE HOUSE, situated on 127 acres of hilly farmland with woods and orchards, has ten somewhat rustic cabins and a restaurant on the property, plus a 30-acre lake "with some of the finest fishing around." Boats are tied up at the dock, waiting for your pleasure. "We've always enjoyed the hospitality, peace and quiet of the area," asserts a guest who's vacationed here for 20 years. "The Brokers (who have taken over recently as new hosts) are pleasant and most accommodating." Hike through the hills and forests, enjoy outdoor games, the children's playground, a rec room with TV. You're near stables, movies and dancing, historical sites and other tourist attractions.

□ Accom. 30 guests in 5 dbls. in farmhouse w./shared bath, & 10 cabins w./pvt. baths. Daily MAP: $20/person. C to 10 yrs.: $3/day & meals ½-price. Also weekly rates. 110 mi. NW of NYC—take NY Thruway to exit 16, W on Rt. 17 to Monticello, W on Rt. 17B to Cochecton, 3 mi. W on Rt. 371 to Tyler Hill. Meet bus in Honesdale, no chg. *The Broker Family, Silver Lake House, Star Rt., Tyler Hill, Pennsylvania 18469. Tel.: (717) 224-4974 or 4688. Open May–Oct. Area 3.*

SPRUCE LANE MOTOR LODGE scarcely looks like a motel—it's an old Lancaster County barn in a quiet rural setting, remodeled for guests on property originally deeded by William Penn to its first owner. "Exceptionally clean," reports a visitor. "The foyer is a large sitting room with furniture grouped for easy get-acquainted seating." Two teenagers in the host family. Tennis court, hiking and bicycle riding. Amish farms and Pennsylvania Dutch dining nearby. The Wenriches will all help you plan your regional sightseeing.

□ Accom. 40 guests in air-cond. motel-type units w./TV for 4-5, pvt. baths. Daily EP Jul. & Aug.: $28 for 2, $3 ea. addl. (to 6 yrs. free); other months—$22 for 2, $3 ea. addl. 150 mi. SW of NYC; 6 mi. E of Lancaster—go E on Rt. 30 to Rt. 340, E 3 mi. to lodge. *Jay & Mazie Wenrich, Spruce Lane Motor Lodge, Smoketown, Pennsylvania 17576. Tel.: (717) 393-1991. Open Apr.-Dec. Area 9.*

SWA-NEA ACRES, a 200-acre dairy farm, invites you to enjoy a full farm life or relax in its quiet valley surrounded by mountains. See how crops are grown and harvested (corn, wheat, oats, barley), bottlefeed a new calf, help feed other animals (ponies, chickens, ducks) or join the farm hands in the fields. You can play badminton, take pony cart rides, do some fishing or just stare at the sunset. "Enjoyed working, living, eating scrumptious meals, playing and talking with our wonderful hosts, '' recalls a guest. "A beautiful farm." And the Neagleys add, "You really get in touch with nature here—life is always changing." Pennsylvania Dutch cooking, including potato pancakes and pot pie, Sara's specialty. Non-smokers preferred.

☐ 6 dbls. in guest house, shared baths, accom. 16 guests. Weekly AP: A $125, C $95. Also weekend rates. 30 mi. N of Harrisburg—take Rt. 147 N to Halifax, Rt. 225 N to 1 mi. past Elizabethville, lane on left. Meet bus in Millersburg, $5/person. *Donald & Sara Neagley, Swa-Nea Acres, R.D., Elizabethville, Pennsylvania 17023. Tel.: (717) 362-8013. Open Apr.-Nov. Area 6.*

VERDANT VIEW FARM is a 94-acre dairy and crop family farm in Lancaster County. Donald and Ginnie (their children are the fourth generation here) have room in the 1896 farmhouse to offer "bed and breakfast" to several families. "Breakfast" means whole wheat crumb pies, omelettes and fresh milk. "Only got one rule," says Donald, "no smoking indoors." Otherwise you're free to do as you please—help with the milking and haying, feed the animals, hike the "back forty" or go sightseeing. "Location-wise, it's in the middle of much," reports an enthusiastic guest recalling the Pennsylvania Dutch area. International folks are welcome—hosts lived in Brazil five years. Sundays they may invite you to the Mennonite service.

☐ Air-cond. rooms w./1 bath accom. 3–4 families. Daily, $10 1 bed, $5 2nd bed, $3 bunk bed; breakfast $1.50-$2. 15 mi. SE of Lancaster—E on Rt. 30, S on Rt. 896, left 1 mi. on Rt. 741, 3rd farm on left after Strasburg R.R. Can arrange pickup. *Donald & Virginia Ranck, Verdant View Farm, R. 1, Box 28, Paradise, Pennsylvania 17562. Tel.: (717) 687-7353 or 8119. Open all year. Area 9.*

THE WATER COMPANY (they'll explain the name) is a 165-acre farm where the young owners invite guests "to share a lifestyle that is fading from contemporary America." Besides raising crops and a variety of farm animals—activities in which guests may lend a hand—Ken is a caseworker and auctioneer, and Sally a phys ed teacher and seller of wood stoves. "Their love for the animals and the land is contagious," reports a vacationer who got involved with painting the house, "and their rooms are comfortable and clean." With no planned schedule, you are free to hike into adjacent state forest land, pick berries

Dyberry Glen, Pennsylvania

and go fishing, bird watching, boating, swimming, cycling, golfing or to weekend auctions. Buggy rides on the farm evenings, and horseback riding if you're experienced.

☐ Accom. 1 family in 3 dbl. rooms (share bath); also rustic cabins w./privy. AP, Sun. p.m. to Sat. a.m.: A $100, C $65. 200 mi. W of New York City. From Harrisburg, go NW on US 15 and 22, NE on US 522 to McClure, N on hardtop rd. 4 mi. Meet plane/bus in Selinsgrove & Lewistown, $20/carload. *Ken & Sally Hassinger, The Water Co., R.D. 2, McClure, Pennsylvania 17841. Tel.: (717) 658-6845. Open Jun. thru Aug. Area 5.*

WINDMERE FARM consists of 250 rolling acres, mostly hay and corn, with a 200-year-old stone farmhouse that's been in the family 100 years. "It's a place to come if you'd like to join a fine, hard-working family (children 10 to 17) who offer minimum comforts and maximum friendliness," a guest explains. "Once I got past the appearance of the old farmhouse, I found truly warm, happy people and came away enriched." You may help with the chores, take a dip in the pool, fish in a stream or just enjoy the peace and quiet. Catherine does lots of baking—bread, cakes, pies and cookies. Nearby in the beautiful

Dyberry Glen, Pennsylva

area are covered and humpback bridges, old mills, old houses; 30 miles to Gettysburg.

☐ Accom. 1 family, dbl. rooms, shared bath. Weekly AP: A $95, C $20–$60. 75 mi. SW of Harrisburg, 20 mi. NW of Hagerstown (Maryland). From I-81, take Greencastle exit, Rt. 16 W to 2 mi. past Upton. *Joel & Catherine Thomas, Windmere Farm, 7629 Buchanan Trail West, Mercersburg, Pennsylvania 17236. Tel.: (717) 328-3407. Open all year. Area 8.*

WINDMILL FARM is where Purebred Hereford beef cattle and sheep graze on 106 acres of rolling land, but it's the vacationers who appreciate the lovely views of the Blue Mountains and the peaceful atmosphere of this well-organized farm. The industrious Becks, their children grown, provide a spacious cottage for guests who hear the comforting creak of the windmill out front when the wind blows. Also comforting are Jennie's breakfasts. "Just can't say enough about the place," a guest reports. Walk through meadows and woods, fish or swim in the pond, or take in resort activities of the Poconos and Amish Dutch Country.

☐ Air-cond. cottage w./bedrooms & baths for 3 guests; fully equipped incl. linens. Daily for 3, $30; weekly, $150. No chg. for

berry Glen, Pennsylvania

breakfast. 129 mi. W of New York City. From I-78 take Rt. 309 N 35 mi. *Peter & Jennie Beck, Windmill Farm, R.D. 1, Box 95, New Ringgold, Pennsylvania 17960. Tel.: (717) 386-4701. Open May thru Oct. Area 6.*

WYANT ACRES, a 327-acre working dairy farm with hay, oats and corn, isn't all spruced up for vacationers. Art describes it as "just a plain old country farm." But he and his wife and 12-year-old son like people and show them real hospitality. While staying in their efficiency apartment, with a stove and refrigerator off to the side, you can explore the hills and take in rural events such as county fairs, livestock auctions, yard sales and festivals. Or go swimming and trout fishing. Wintertime means sledding and tobogganing on the farm.

   □ Apt. w./2 rooms, bath, cooking facilities. Daily EP: A $7.50, C $2; weekly, A $47.50, C $10. Call evenings. 82 mi. NE of Pittsburgh. From New Bethlehem, go W on Rt. 861, right on Squirrel Rd., keep right on dirt rd., 1 mi. right at bottom of hill. Meet plane in DuBois, $20/carload, bus in New Bethlehem, $5. *Art & Imogene Wyant, Wyant Acres, R.D. 2, Box 128, New Bethlehem, Pennsylvania 16242. Tel.: (814) 275-3892. Open all year. Area 4.*

South Dakota

The largest remaining buffalo herd on the continent roams the southern Black Hills, revered by the Indians as sacred ground, and sets the mood for the wide open cattle and farm country of South Dakota. Here, too, is the Homestake Mine, largest producing gold mine in the Western Hemisphere, and Mt. Rushmore, now famous for the gigantic carved heads of four presidents. The carving of the weird cliffs and ravines at the Badlands National Monument, however, was sculptured by water, wind and volcanic action. South Dakota's gold rush came in 1876, and statehood thirteen years later.

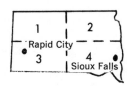

CROSS RANCH is a 400-acre ranch where the Neubergers raise cattle, sheep, geese and pigs and invite a few guests at a time to experience "a slow, nature-centered life on a Christian ranch farm." Guests are expected to pitch in, not only with chores but in family recreation activities, and to share family prayers and Bible study. The terrain turns hilly in the pasture by the lake where much of the sport activity takes place. Ruth prepares all meals from scratch and even spins her own yarn. Overnight guests are welcome as space permits. Non-smokers, non-drinkers, preferred.

☐ Accom. 8 guests, shared bath. AP rates: $95/week, $50/weekend, $5/overnight w./breakfast. 28 mi. W of Sioux Falls—go 3½ mi. S at I-90 exit 374. Meet bus in Canistota, no chg. *Tom & Ruth Neuberger, Cross Ranch, Canistota, South Dakota 57012. Tel.: (605) 296-3314. Open all year. Area 4.*

SKOGLUND FARM makes an ideal stopover if you're traveling on Interstate 90—or flying into the area. You'll see how a 1,000-

Skoglund Farm, South Dakota

acre cattle and grain farm is run, join the family for meals
(Swedish cooking a specialty), feed the animals, rock hunt, go
horseback riding or relax. "We ate supper and breakfast with
the Skoglunds, and then she packed enough food for our picnic
lunch plus more," states a vacationing couple who passed by
recently and spent the night. "It's a perfect place to unwind and
get treated like family instead of like tourists."

☐ Accom. 16 guests in 5 farmhouse bedrooms, shared baths.
Daily AP: A $15, C $10, incl. riding. 50 mi. NW of Sioux
Falls—go 34 mi. W on I-90 to Salem exit, 12 mi. N and 3 mi. W.
Meet plane in Mitchell or Sioux Falls, bus in Salem. *Alden &
Delores Skoglund, Skoglund Farm, Rt. 2, Canova, South Da-
kota 53231. Tel.: (605) 247-3445. Open all year. Area 4.*

Texas

If you tell a Texan that the "Land of the Cowboy" extends on north through Wyoming, he's quick to agree. After all, the whole area was Texas before Texas joined the Union in 1845, and before it sold to the Government land that now is part of Wyoming, Colorado, New Mexico, Oklahoma and Kansas. But Texas still is big—largest of all the states until Alaska edged it into second place. There are vast ranchlands, and every community has its horse shows, livestock auctions and rodeos. The Spanish, French, Mexican, Texan and Confederate flags have flown here. Typically Texas, on the rangelands, is the sight of cows among the oil derricks.

CAMP CHAPARRAL invites families and groups to share the best of two worlds—farm and ranch life, and modern facilities as well. Guests are welcomed throughout the year except for June through August when the ranch is reserved for young folks only (see chapter, "For Teens and Under"). Take part in roundups and branding or whatever other activities are going on in the wild brush country. "It's a delightful bit of the Old West," exclaims a guest. "This is rural Texas—air-conditioned and awash with a swimming pool!" Roller rink, riding arena, trails, fishing, tennis, wildlife, hayrides and campfires. Non-smokers preferred.

□ Accom. 6 families or up to 50 guests in air-cond. cabins. Daily AP: A $25, C $12–$15 (to 3 yrs., free); sr. citizen, $15. Riding incl. 50 mi S of San Antonio—go S 46 mi. on Rt. 16, E on Rt. 140 to 1 mi. beyond Christine, right at camp sign. Meet plane in San Antonio, $10/carload; bus in Pleasanton, no chg. *Ernest & Bettie Seiffert, Camp Chaparral, Box 30, Christine,*

Texas 78012. Tel.: (512) 784-3233. Open Jan.–May, Sep.–Nov. Area 9.

LAZY HILLS GUEST RANCH. The pace is slow at this cattle ranch in scenic Hill Country, but there's still plenty to do—and it all "looks mighty fine from the saddle." Trail rides four times a day, an Olympic-sized pool, tennis courts, archery, putting green, game room, cookouts, fishing and birding. "The trail rides were outstanding. Our kids had a ball. Guest rooms are not plush, but clean and comfortable," declares a visitor. Another adds, "What a warm, friendly place—such a sense of relaxation and peace of mind." Schools, churches, clubs and conventions—such as a recent "Painters' Holiday"—find the ranch's Brown Palace ideal for seminars and retreats. The area features a summer theater, golf, art shows and caverns.

  ☐ Accom. 26–94 guests in 26 air-cond. units w./fireplace & pvt. bath. Daily AP: $56/couple, C less. Riding incl. w./weekly rates. 75 mi. NW of San Antonio—NW on I-10 to Kerrville, 8 mi. W on Rt. 27, 1½ mi. NW to ranch. Meet plane in San Antonio, $35 up to 4; bus in Kerrville, no chg. *Bob & Carol Steinruck, Lazy Hills Guest Ranch, Box F, Ingram, Texas 78025. Tel.: (512) 367-5600. Open all year. Area 6.*

Weaver Ranch, Texas

WEAVER RANCH, a fourth-generation, family-owned cattle ranch, invites families and adults to enjoy its activities in fall, winter and spring. (In summer, the guest list is limited to young people only—see "For Teens and Under" chapter.) These are cordial, knowledgeable, outgoing hosts. Shirley's special interest is in antiques—"the house is tastefully decorated with them," a visitor points out. But the real involvement here is in cattle ranching and rodeos. "When folks leave us," the Weavers observe, "we hope they take with them a greater love for the land and creatures, learning the fun and work and fulfillment of our nation's great cattle industry."

☐ Accom. 10 guests in ranch house, shared baths. Weekly AP: A $175, C $80, incl. riding. 80 mi. S of Dallas—go S on I-45 and Hwy. 14, turn W on Farm Rd. 27 to ranch sign. Meet plane in Dallas, $20/carload; bus in Corsicana, $5. *Ted & Shirley Weaver, Weaver Ranch, Rt. 1, Wortham, Texas 76693. Tel.: (817) 765-3489. Open all year. Area 7.*

WHISPERING WINDS GUEST RANCH features spacious, attractively furnished cottages for guests. Each has a fireplace in the large living room, two bedrooms and baths, and a well-equipped kitchen and dining area. They are well spaced for privacy, with well-kept lawns. "We do little to entertain," the Hevenors emphasize, "but you'll find horses and a wrangler for morning rides and free pony rides for the small fry." The Medina River and Julian Creek supply anglers with bass, catfish and rough fish, and there's a swimming pool. Century-old oaks, groves of pecan and cypress dot the central Texas countryside. An 18-hole golf course, two tennis courts and an excellent restaurant on the adjoining ranch.

☐ Housekeeping cottages (6). Weekly AP: $180–$225/unit. Riding extra. 42 mi. W of San Antonio—take Bandera exit off Loop 410, ask at any service station. Meet plane/bus in San Antonio, $5/person. *Phil & Martha Hevenor, Whispering Winds, Bandera, Texas 78003. Tel.: (512)796-3220. Open all year. Area 8.*

Navajo Cliffs Ranch, Utah

Utah

Colorful pinnacles and sheer cliffs rising from Lake Powell's blue waters, deep canyons carved by the Colorado and other great rivers, red-rock buttes and spires, enormous dinosaur bones protruding from a cliff, pre-Columbian pictorglyphs and petroglyphs on canyon walls, Indian reservations, salt and alkali deserts, fertile valleys, forested, towering mountains—all are part of an area that has fast become known for its river runs, backpacking, mountain climbing, skiing, horseback riding, jeep trips, water sports and fabulous beauty. In 1847 the Mormons settled here, and in 1896 Utah received statehood.

NAVAJO CLIFFS RANCH, with 10,000 acres, borders Zion National Park, and its terrain is similar to that amazingly scenic park area. Here Russ and his parents raise crops and livestock and provide a lodge for guests. "Horse riding is our major activity," he explains. "These rides range from two hours to four days, camping out. We also offer four-wheel-drive tours to Indian ruins and to four national parks, and we take covered wagon trips for several days." On these excursions Russ' father is the head Dutch oven cook, with 50 years of experience behind him. "The atmosphere was relaxed but the activities were many," advises a guest. "Meals were fantastic and we had a super good time. The children still talk about Russ and the ranch."

☐ Lodge accom. for 12 guests, share 2 baths. Weekly AP: A $335, C $175; C w./o. parents, $220; incl. riding & tours. Also daily rates. 20 mi. N of Kanab. Meet guests there, no chg. Meet plane in Cedar City or St. George, $25/carload. *Russell Keller, Navajo Cliffs Ranch, Box 698, Kanab, Utah 84741. Tel.: (801) 644-2125. Open May–Sep. Area 3.*

Knoll Farm Country Inn, Vermont

Vermont

In 1609 Samuel de Champlain explored westward from the Canadian coast and came to the beautiful lake which bears his name. There was much battling between the English settlers, who organized the famous Green Mountain Boys, and the Indians, the French, the people of northern New York and the British—a history hard to imagine in pastoral, peaceful Vermont today. In 1801 it became a state. Typical of this Green Mountains state today are winding backroads, green valleys, rivers, lakes, antiques, church spires and picturesque villages.

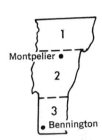

BELL-MOTT-BEACH COTTAGES are at the northern end of Lake Champlain, close to the Canadian border. "The lake here is four miles across," writes Abner Mott, "with a beautiful view of the Adirondack Mountains and sunsets that are out of this world." He has a quarter mile of private sandy beach plus horseshoes, badminton and volleyball courts. Guests stay in comfortable, heated housekeeping cottages, each with an outdoor picnic table and a boat. Fishing is "some of the best in the North Country"—bass, northern pike and pan-fish—and there's a golf course and riding stable a few miles away. It's a short walk to stores, churches and the laundromat, and a scenic drive to Lake Placid, Stowe, Montreal and other nearby spots.

☐ Cottages (6) w./2 bedrooms each, $150/week EP incl. linens. 45 mi. N of Burlington, 45 mi. S of Montreal (Canada). From New York City take Thruway to Albany, Northway to Champlain (New York) exit, E on Rt. 11 to US 2, 4 mi. to beach. Meet plane in Burlington, $10/carload, train/bus in St. Albans, no chg. *Abner & Luella Mott, Bell-Mott-Beach Cottages, Alburg, Vermont 05440. Tel.: (802) 796-3623. Open Jun.–Oct. Area 1.*

BROOK BOUND LODGE & CHALETS occupy 33 secluded acres with beautiful views of Haystack and Mt. Snow. These and other fine ski slopes are minutes away, beckoning families to this friendly, informal lodge. For summer guests there's a heated pool, clay court tennis, lawn games, fishing and canoeing on mountain streams and lakes, hiking along fabled country trails. Generous home-cooked meals with fresh-from-the-garden vegetables. "I'm always flattered when people ask for my recipes," notes Betty Fajans, "I know I'm on the right track. I usually give them out freely and ask for recipes in return." Guests stress the charming accommodations, the excellent meals, the pleasant hosts. Interesting Vermont shops, maple candy factories, harness racing, museums, fairs, auctions, golf, theater, and Marlboro Music Festival nearby.

☐ Lodge rooms for 20 guests, pvt. baths. Summer weekly MAP: A $132–$152, C $75–$108. Also daily rates. Chalets for 6–11: weekly EP (spring thru fall) $165–$240; entire season Dec.–Apr., $2,400–$3,000 EP. 200 mi. N of NYC, 20 mi. E of Bennington. Take NY Thruway to exit 24, Northway, NY 7, E on VT 9 to Wilmington. Meet bus in Wilmington, no chg. *The Fajans, Brook Bound Lodge & Chalets, Box F-Coldbrook Rd., Wilmington, Vermont 05363. Tel.: (802) 464-5267. Open all year. Area 3.*

HILL'S FARM INN was built in 1830 and moved by 40 yoke of oxen to its present site next to a dairy farm and near a scenic village. "The country roads and rolling hills make it an excellent area for biking and hiking," advises Barbara Hill, "and for artists and photographers." The Southern Vermont Art Center is in the village. "It's a place you want to return to," declares a guest—"delicious meals, a lovely farm inn—quiet with beautiful views." Only a quarter mile away is Battenkill, one of New England's best trout streams. Skiers flock to the area in season, with Bromley, Stratton, Magic Mountain and Snow Valley nearby.

☐ Accom. 25 guests in farmhouse rooms & cabins, pvt. baths. Weekly AP, $110–$125; daily $18–$22; C less. 200 mi. NE of NYC. From Bennington on US 7, go N 18½ mi., right on Sunderland Rd. Meet plane in Albany or Rutland, train in Brattleboro, reas. chg.; bus in Arlington or Manchester, no chg. *Howard & Barbara Hill, Hill's Farm Inn, Rt. 2, Arlington, Vermont 05250. Tel.: (802) 375-2269. Open May–Oct. & ski seas. Area 3.*

KNOLL FARM COUNTRY INN considers its biggest asset the exchange of fellowship and spiritual growth, especially in mealtime conversations. The popularity of the Farm's peaceful, friendly, old-time atmosphere keeps the farmhouse booked six months or more in advance, especially for summer, mostly with couples and singles, including older people. "It's a very special place," notes a visitor, "—such a generosity of spirit on the part of the owners—very remarkable." You're apt to run into a chess game or poetry-writing, go on nature walks, swimming or boating, ride in a carriage or on horseback and feed the animals. Guests come from everywhere. "Only five bedrooms," one of them points out, "so the group is congenial and never large." Prefer no smoking.

☐ Accom. 10 guests in farmhouse rooms, shared baths. Summer, weekly AP: A $140, C $90. Also daily & MAP winter rates. Riding extra. 190 mi. N of Boston; 23 mi. S of Montpelier—go S on Rts. 100B and 100 to Waitsfield. Meet plane in Burlington, $20/carload; train in Waterbury or plane/bus in Montpelier, no chg. *Bill & Ann Day Heinzerling, Knoll Farm Country Inn, Box 88-BG, Bragg Hill, Waitsfield, Vermont 05673. Tel.: (802) 496-3939. Open all but Apr. & Nov. Area 2.*

Brook Bound Lodge & Chalets, Vermont

MELIS FARMS, a 600-acre cattle farm in the Green Mountains, is full of 19th-century charm. The 1820 house has a cooking fireplace and oven—modern facilities are hidden from view. The 1896 house, a well-preserved Victorian with Franklin and wood-burning cook stoves, is furnished and decorated to the period. The 1972 house, on a quiet and secluded brook, features pine-board walls, screened porch and 2-car garage. All three are beautifully maintained, with fireplaces, new electric appliances, enjoyable summer and winter. "Lovely country houses," remarks a guest. Near Mt. Snow and Stratton, good x-country skiing, and a Morgan horse breeding farm and riding school where you can ride and board your horse.

☐ Accom. 30 guests in 3 fully equipped guest farmhouses, ea. w./2 baths, 4-5 bedrooms, living room, kitchen, washer/dryer. EP rates per unit: $200/week, $650/month, $2,750/ski season. 28 mi. NW of Brattleboro—go N on Rt. 30 & S 5 mi. on Rt. 100 to Wardsboro. *F.K. Melis, Melis Farms, Wardsboro, Vermont 05355. Tel.: (802) 896-4701. Or call NYC office: (212) 977-9500. Open all year. Area 3.*

MERRY MEADOW FARM is home to Thoroughbreds and Morgan horses, and to the exceptional Williams family who also breed Australian Shepherds and have a regular supply of furry barn cats and kittens. The 200-acre working horse farm borders the Connecticut River, so canoeing is an activity here, and there's a heated pool. But mainly things revolve around learning to ride in the outdoor rings or indoor arena and going out on scenic trails. "They're a family of uncommon talent and character," reports a guest, "and provide excellent riding facilities and scrumptious family-style meals." You're minutes from Dartmouth, auctions, theaters, fairs, square dancing and ski slopes. Children 10 to 16 only July to mid-August—see chapter, "For Teens and Under." Families come other times, including spring, fall foliage and ski seasons.

☐ Farmhouse rooms, shared baths, for 8 guests; bunkhouse for small groups. Weekly AP: A $196, C to 6 yrs., $140; also MAP & daily rates. 150 mi. NW of Boston. At Bradford (exit 16 on I-91), turn right on Rt. 25 to US 5, S 1½ mi. Meet plane in Lebanon or train/bus in White River Jct., $10/carload; bus in Bradford, no chg. *Jack & Betty Williams, Merry Meadow Farm, Bradford, Vermont 05033. Tel.: (802) 222-4412. Open all year. Area 2.*

REEVESDALE FARM is a working dairy farm, a warm friendly place to stay, where guests can get involved or just sit

Merry Meadow Farm, Vermont

back and relax. "Buck and Hilda are wonderful hosts, and completely relaxed with all types of persons," writes a guest who's stayed with them many years. "You'll be surprised at how quickly you get to know the local 'Vermonters'." You'll also savor Hilda's donuts, pies and breads and the farm-fresh vegetables. When you're not helping to look after the 70 Holsteins or the saddle horse or pony, you can fish in the farm's brook or the White River, or visit the town swimming pool, auctions, antiques shops, horse farms and other places in the picturesque area. In winter, bring your skis.

☐ Accom. 8–10 guests in 5 farmhouse rooms, 2 shared baths. Weekly MAP: A $100, C less. Daily MAP: A $15, C 4–12 yrs., $4–$12. 19 mi. N of White River Junction—take Sharon exit off I-89, Rts. 14 and 110 to Tunbridge, right 3 mi. opposite Town Clerk's office. Meet plane/bus in White River Jct., $10/carload. *Reeve & Hilda Rogers, Reevesdale Farm, Tunbridge, Vermont 05077. Tel.: (802) 889-3370. Open all year. Area 2.*

RODGERS DAIRY FARM is operated by three generations of the Rodgers Family on 500 acres which their Scottish ancestors settled in the early 1800s. Guests watch the cows being milked by machine, go on haywagon rides, ride the horses, pull weeds, gather vegetables, help with the haying or just sit in lawn chairs under the maple tree. Or they drive a few miles to Shadow Lake for a swim or poke around nearby Glover and West Glover with a combined population of 600 inhabitants. Lots of farm animals for children to play with. "We loved the simple hominess," recalls a guest, "—the restful evenings on the front porch, the hearty meals, but most of all the Rodgers family—that's what calls us back each year."

□ Accom. 10 guests in 5 dbls., shared baths. Weekly AP: A $120, C $60. 240 mi. NW of Boston—take I-93 & I-91 N to Barton & phone. Meet bus in Barton, no chg. *John & Ruth— John W. & Marie—Rodgers, Rodgers Dairy Farm, West Glover, Vermont 05875. Tel.: (802) 525-6677. Open Jun.–Nov. Area 1.*

WEATHERVANE LODGE (near Mt. Snow and Haystack) fills up with skiers—both x-country and downhill—during the winter months. The rest of the year this friendly little lodge is wide open for vacationers. At the edge of the Green Mountain Forest, the property was one of Vermont's first farms. "What a pleasant place to stay while touring this delightful area!" exclaims a visitor. "The Chabots go to great lengths to make each guest feel welcome." Great country hiking nearby, plus tennis, golf, riding, lake swimming, fishing, canoeing, sailing, antiques shops.

□ Accom. 30 guests in lodge rooms & suite, pvt. & shared baths. Daily rates: summer incl. breakfast, $8–$17; winter MAP, $14–$28. Also 4-bedroom fully equipped house on lake w./rowboat, Jun.–Sep., $175/week. 200 mi. N of NYC, 130 mi. NW of Boston. From Wilmington, go N on Rt. 100 to Dunn's Store, 1 mi. right on Dorr Fitch Rd. Meet bus in Wilmington, no chg. *Ernie & Liz Chabot, Weathervane Lodge, 150 Dorr Fitch Rd., West Dover, Vermont 05356. Tel.: (802) 464-5426. Open all year. Area 3.*

WHITETAIL CORNERS GUEST HOUSE was a one-room schoolhouse which Gus and Madeleine have remodeled and expanded with excellent taste and fine workmanship. The large living room with its handsome stone fireplace opens onto an L-shaped deck where you can drop a line into a stream and catch a trout for breakfast. Meals are family style with homemade bread, pies, jams, jellies and lots more. A pony and rabbits live in the barn. It's a fascinating area for auctions, antiques, local events and square dances every Saturday night. Cross-country skiing, snowshoeing, snowmobiling and ice fishing in winter.

□ Accom. 8 guests in 3 dbl. rooms sharing 2 baths. Daily rates/person: $20 AP, $17.25 MAP, $12–$15 w./1 meal. 20 mi.

NW of White River Junction—go W on I-89, exit 2, W on Rt. 14, right on Rt. 110 to Tunbridge, right at Town Clerk's office for 3 mi. Meet plane in Lebanon (New Hampshire), $10/carload; bus in White River Jct., $10. *Gus & Madeleine Linde, Whitetail Corners Guest House, Potash Rd., Tunbridge, Vermont 05077. Tel: (802) 889-5565. Open all year. Area 2.*

WINDHAM HILL FARM is set in open fields with magnificent views of the West River valley. The nearly 140-year-old farmhouse is restored with fireplaces and cheerful rooms and furnished with antiques. Here the Seagers and their children (in their 20s) are the genial hosts. You settle into a happy routine of swimming, riding, playing tennis, bird watching, and in the evening, family-style candlelight dinners. There are fairs, church suppers, the Marlboro Festival or barn dances to attend. Or you can just read a book. Kiddies have a sandbox and frog pond and are served an early dinner around the kitchen table. In winter: ice skating, tobogganing, x-country and downhill skiing at nearby slopes.

□ Accom. 20–25 guests in farmhouse rooms, most w./pvt. bath. Weekly MAP: $125–$162 each, dbl. occup. Daily & family rates. 120 mi. NW of Boston. From Brattleboro, go 21 mi. N on Hwy. 30 to W. Townshend, 1¼ mi. N on Windham Rd. Meet bus in Brattleboro. *Jim & Betty Seagers, Windham Hill Farm, West Townshend, Vermont 05359. Tel.: (802) 874-5151 or 5951. Open May–Oct. & Dec.–Apr. Area 3.*

Knoll Farm Country Inn, Vermont

Virginia

Charlottesville
Richmond
1 2 3 4 5 6

Virginia is pure history in a scenic, pastoral setting. In every valley and rolling plain, restored villages and old churches, shrines and battlefields, covered bridges, plantation gardens, country stores and pioneer homes tell the story of America. Settlers came to Jamestown in 1607. Five years later began the sad practice of slavery. Patrick Henry's shouts for liberty, Thomas Jefferson's drafting of the Declaration of Independence, the leadership of George Washington, Robert E. Lee, and others—all have fashioned the nation's history as well as that of the state.

COVE MOUNTAIN GOAT DAIRY is the only Grade A goat dairy in Virignia, with its goat population at 164. "We milk, pasteurize, bottle and distribute the milk in this area," report the Wohlfords, former educators. "Our lives have become centered around the goats, and our farm is not just primitive—it's crude! You'll be walking in mud, and if you're not accustomed to wood heat in a drafty farmhouse we recommend coming between April and September." Visiting the Wohlfords is a unique experience—"like a farm of the 1850s, only with electricity," explains a guest. "Mary Clare and Bill are hardworking, terrific people. I went there because I wanted to milk the goats, ride the tractor and help mow the fields. It was like pioneering, with cultured and warm hosts." Guests also visit auctions and take hikes in the adjoining Jefferson National Forest.

☐ Accom. family of 4 (children over 5 yrs.) in bunkhouse w./outhouse, & addl. bedroom & shower in farmhouse. Weekly AP: A $120, C $85; daily rates. 300 mi. W of Washington DC,

75 mi. SW of Roanoke—take I-81 S to Wytheville. Meet bus in Wytheville, no chg. *Bill & Mary Clare Wohlford, Cove Mountain Goat Dairy, Rt. 2, Box 255-A, Wytheville, Virginia 24382. Tel.: (703) 228-3379. Open all year. Area 4.*

DEER TRACKS LODGE. Are you planning a family reunion? A business meeting? A holiday with a group of friends? You can be undisturbed at this mountain lodge surrounded by woodland with a 5-acre lake, rowboat, trout stream, badminton, horse-shoes and other games. It's a split-level house—5 bedrooms, 2 baths, 2 living rooms (a fireplace in each), screened porch and kitchen—comfortable and homey with country auction furniture. "A spacious lodge," according to a guest, "outstanding in every respect. Quiet, isolated, yet plenty to do." A short drive to movies, roller skating, bowling, golf, historic Charlottesville, Monticello, Luray Caverns and marvelous antiquing. Your hosts, 15 miles from the lodge, will be on hand for your arrival.

   ☐ Lodge for group up to 14. Daily EP: $38–$43 up to 9, $4–$5 ea. addl. 13 mi. SW of Harrisonburg. *Dan Stickley, Jr., Deer Tracks Lodge, Rt. 10, Box 306, Harrisonburg, Virginia 22801. Tel.: (703) day, 434-6791; night, 433-1360. Open all year. Area 2.*

GRAVES' MOUNTAIN LODGE is on 5,000 acres with orchards, crops and livestock in the Blue Ridge Mountains near Shenandoah National Park and the Rapidan Wildlife Area. No structured activities program, but there is a Jr. Olympic-sized swimming pool, tennis courts, riding, hiking, trout fishing and rock hunting. "I enjoyed the absolute informality," notes a guest, "—no 'social director,' but rustic country atmosphere, superb mountain views, friendly hosts and outstanding meals." People come from miles around just to feast on Rachel's farm-fresh foods—specialties such as fried chicken and country ham, served family- or buffet-style. Near the Skyline Drive and Charlottesville.

   ☐ Accom. 100 guests in rustic & historic cabins (some w./fireplace), new motel units w./pvt. bath & air-cond., & farmhouse. Weekly AP: A $135–$190, C $60. Riding extra. Also EP rates & 2 conference rooms. 85 mi. S of Washington, D.C.— go S on US 29 to 7 mi. S of Culpeper, 12 mi. W on rd. 609, 1 mi. N on Rt. 231, 4 mi. W on rd. 670. Meet plane in Charlottesville or train in Orange, $10/carload; bus in Madison, no chg. *Jim & Rachel Graves, Graves' Mountain Lodge, Syria, Virginia 22743. Tel.: (703) 923-4231. Open Apr.–Nov. Area 2.*

MONTFAIR FAMILY RESORT & FARM adjoins a 1,400-acre farm and the unspoiled woods and mountains of Shenandoah National Park. A spring-fed lake with sandy beaches (and lifeguards) separates the cedar housekeeping cottages and campsites. "I sit on the porch," writes a guest, "reading all the books I don't have time for all year, while my husband and two children hike, ride horseback and swim." Also on the property are tennis, fishing in four stocked lakes and ponds, wagon rides, paddleboats, volleyball, softball, a rec hall and overnight campout trail rides to the top of the Blue Ridge. Many activities in this region of country auctions, horse shows and crafts, and an abundance of historic places to visit.

☐ Accom. in 9 cottages (up to 6 in each). Daily EP, $36–$42 for family of 4, each addl. $2.50–$5. Weekly EP: $195–$220 for 4, addl. $10–$25. Fully equipped incl. linens. Also 68 campsites. 15 mi. NW of Charlottesville—from US 29, take Barracks Rd. W for 11 mi., then N on Rt. 810 4 mi. Meet plane/train/bus in Charlottesville. *Phillip & Mary Sheridan, Montfair Family Resort & Farm, Rt. 2, Box 383, Crozet, Virginia 22932. Tel.: (804) 823-5202. Open all year. Area 2.*

ROUNTON FARM offers a tastefully-decorated snug cottage, with two bedrooms, living room, kitchen and bath large enough for three guests. "It's a delightful place for people who love privacy, the beauties of nature, walks, birds, trees, hills, and vistas," comments a guest. The Obers run a small calf-cow-steer operation and do some haying. Their children are 8 and 10. For participators they promise that "nobody will be excluded from helping during the hay season or when cattle need to be moved." You can fish in the pond, hike and ride if you bring your own horse. Community tennis courts, swimming pool and excellent library in Orange. It's an hour's drive to Charlottesville or the Blue Ridge Mountains, and two hours to Washington.

☐ Fully equipped cottage, $25/day or $125/week, EP. 90 mi. S of Washington, D.C., 32 mi. NE of Charlottesville. From Orange RR Stn., go E on E. Main St., (which becomes Rapidan Rd.) for 2½ mi. Meet plane in Charlottesville, $10/carload; train/bus in Orange, no chg. *Donald & Vibeke Ober, Rounton Farm, P.O. Box 6, Orange, Virginia 22960. Tel.: (703) 672-2793. Open all year. Area 2.*

SHENANDOAH VALLEY FARM offers fully-equipped housekeeping cottages with fireplaces in a scenic and historic area off Skyline Drive. The Dixons raise Black Angus cattle on their 225 acres—half pasture, half woodland, with springs, a

Rounton Farm, Virginia

stream and many birds. "We have our own small mountain," they report, "where you can enjoy hiking and picnicking." There's a nice farm pond for swimming and fishing, and a lighted all-weather tennis court. "It's an ideal retreat to write, think and relax in," suggests a visitor. "The hosts are congenial and the views are beautiful." Less than an hour to Lexington, Staunton, Charlottesville; easy access to Luray Caverns, Monticello, Natural Bridge. Antiques shops and weekly auctions.

☐ Accom. 20 guests in 4 cottages w./fireplace, 2 bedrooms, pvt. bath, kitchen. Daily EP: $25 for 2, ea. addl. $4–$7; your day visitors, $3. 100 mi. SE of Washington, D.C. 10 mi. E of Harrisonburg—go 10 mi. E on Rt. 33, left 1 mi. on Rt. 646. *Charles & Madelyn Dixon, Shenandoah Valley Farm, Rt. 1, Box 76, McGaheysville, Virginia 22840. Tel.: (703) 289-5402. Open all year. Area 1.*

Washington

Explorers from Spain, France, Britain, Russia and America traveled this northwestern area before it became a part of Oregon Territory, then a separate territory, and finally, in 1889, a state. It brought to the Union a great fertile plateau in the eastern half of the state, a coastline of remarkable beauty, and in between, the Cascade Range with peaks that are capped with snow year 'round. It's a breath-taking wilderness—some of it within the bounds of Mt. Rainier and Olympic National Parks—seen from mountain highways, ski slopes and coastal waters or from remote hiking and riding trails.

FLYING L RANCH, about 2 hours from Portland or Yakima, seems as remote as snow-capped Mt. Adams rising majestically before it. Ilse Lloyd, a dedicated conservationist, is as much at home with a paint brush and sketching pad as she is in the well-equipped cookhouse or on her Arabian mount. "A beautiful setting, excellent meals, and cultured and delightful hostess," writes a guest. "No structured entertainment, much to our delight. We ride gentle horses, often see a doe and twin fawns, walk in the moonlight, photograph wildflowers and humming birds, and sometimes go huckleberrying or drive with Ilse to Bird Creek Meadows, one of the most beautiful spots on earth." Dense pine woods are the backdrop for the cluster of white buildings, the corral where you can learn to ride, a children's pond, fishing, games. The huge ranch house living room is a center for music, reading and socializing. Nearby are a salmon hatchery, rodeos, fairs. The ranch is headquarters for the Mt. Adams Wilderness Institute (backpacking and mountaineering experiences).

☐ Accom. 14 guests in cabins & guest rooms, all pvt. baths. Weekly MAP: A $120–$160, C 6–12 yrs. $70–$100, 4–5 $65, 1–3 free. Riding incl. Housekeeping cabin for 4, $175/week EP. 100 mi. NE of Portland—go E on I-80 to Hood River, N on Rt. 141 to Glenwood, ranch sign on right. Meet plane in Portland, $15/carload, train/bus in Hood River, no chg. *Mrs. Ilse Lloyd, Flying L Ranch, Rt. 2, Glenwood, Washington 98619. Tel.: (509) 364-3488. Open May thru Sep. Area 4.*

THE PARTRIDGE INN, built in 1975, is surrounded by pear and apple orchards and vineyards, with magnificent views of mountains, valleys and the Columbia River Gorge. There often are warm homemade glazed yeast doughnuts at breakfast, barbecued Cornish game hen and other specialties at dinner, freshly-made jams, jellies and dressings in the small gift shop, a trampoline and screened gazebo in the yard. "It's a place for quiet people who enjoy mother's cooking and God's creation," explains a guest. Nature lovers, small-town buffs and wilderness explorers find it an endlessly interesting area. Nearby are fish hatcheries, fish ladders for salmon at the dams, and the last

Flying L Ranch, Washington

Flying L Ranch, Washington

working lumber flume in America.

☐ Accom. 1 family. Room & breakfast $25 for 2 persons, $5 ea. addl.; dinners $4-$6. 60 mi. E of Portland (Oregon)—E on I-80N to town of Hood River, cross bridge, left 2 mi. to Cook Underwood Rd., 2 mi. up hill. *Nora E. McNab, The Partridge Inn, Box 100, Underwood, Washington 98651. Tel.: (509) 493-2381. Open all year. Area 4.*

West Virginia

The Shawnee Indians who lived in this land of high, wooded Appalachian Mountains, deep valleys and broad, rolling plateaus discouraged settlers until the early 18th century. The area was part of Virginia through the early 1800s. But when Virginia seceded from the Union at the start of the Civil War, western county delegates declared the action void and in 1863 gained separate recognition as the 35th state. The state is full of parks, rivers, warm spring spas, mountain trails, wildflowers, wildlife, forests, year 'round sports, mountain craftsmen and many reminders of its rugged pioneer history.

VALLEY VIEW FARM is a place where the kids will say "it's a real farm!"—and it is. A picturesque 256 acres with beef cattle and sheep. "It's fine for a family vacation," remarks a guest, "—delicious meals and wonderful hosts." There's lots to see in the area—Lost River State Park (where the river gets lost in a mountain), Rock Creek Lake, trout pond, Blackwater Falls, Cass Scenic Railway, poultry festivals, and home tours in the fall with shows and sales of mountain crafts and antiques. Guests come from all over—"I love people and learn so much from them," Edna reports.

☐ Farmhouse rooms for up to 10 guests & bunkhouse for 10, shared bath. Weekly AP: A $120, C $65; daily A $18, C $10. 136 mi. W of Washington, D.C. From Harrisonburg (Virginia), go N on I-81 or US 11 to Broadway, W 5 mi. on Hwy. 259 to farm S of Mathias. Meet bus in Harrisonburg, reas. chg. *Ernest & Edna Shipe, Valley View Farm, Mathias, West Virginia 26812. Tel.: (304) 897-5229. Open all year. Area 2.*

Wisconsin

Eau Claire 3 Wausau
Madison 6
5 Milwaukee

When Champlain's emissary, Jean Nicolet, landed here in 1634, he was dressed in oriental robes, believing that he had found the fabled Northwest Passage to China. To his dismay, he was greeted by a few non-Chinese Indians. Control of the land passed to the English, then the Americans, and settlers came all the way from the eastern and southern states. It became a state in 1848. Wisconsin's rolling plains are basically agricultural. It is known for its statewide bike route, and for its miles of shoreline on Lake Michigan, Lake Superior, the Mississippi River and thousands of inland lakes.

CAMP LAKE RESORT is for easy-going, quiet vacations and many who come here for a "roughly rustic" life have been returning for years. Spacious grounds, song birds and nature walks are on 120 private acres bordering Nicolet National Forest. A boat comes with each cabin, and the Larsons keep boats you can use on three other good fishing lakes. They are "hard-working people who will leave you to yourselves," comments a guest who has been coming here for years. You are welcome to watch at milking time. There's golf, tennis, riding and a public beach in the area. Especially beautiful in fall. Comfortable cottages, unique in artistic design.

   ☐ Log or stone cottages w./kitchen & pvt. baths (1 w./outhouse) sleep 5 or more; bring linens. Weekly EP: $100/cottage, + $10/adult if more than 2. 85 mi. N of Green Bay—N on US 41, N on Rt. 32 to 8 mi. N of Mountain, W on Maiden Lake Rd. Meet bus in Lakewood, $5/carload. *John & Esther Larson, Camp Lake Resort, R.R. 1, Mountain, Wisconsin 54149. Tel.: (715) 276-6431. Open May thru Oct. Area 4.*

ETHILTON FARMS, with 160 acres of hay, grain, corn and livestock, features a comfortable spacious farmhouse where life is friendly and casual. You'll find riding horses, a pony cart, jeep rides, hayrides, seasonal farm activities, animals to feed and nature hikes. A graduate home economist, Ethel turns out scrumptious meals, with food fresh from their huge garden. (Her book, *Haven O'Bliss,* all about hosting vacationers for 20 years, can be ordered from her for $3.95.) "Some of our fondest memories are of the farm, the Blisses, their hayloft, horses and food," notes a guest. Scenic Kettle Moraine, auctions, fairs, golf, tennis, swimming, fishing and skiing all nearby. Non-drinkers preferred.

☐ Farmhouse rooms for up to 20 guests, shared baths. Daily AP: A $22.50, C $17.50; weekly $140 & $110. Riding incl. 8 mi. SW of Hartford. 120 mi. NW of Chicago—go N on I-94 to Hwy. 83, N to Holy Hill area, 4 mi. W on County Trunk O. Meet plane in Milwaukee, $20/carload; bus in Hartford or Oconomowoc, $3/person. *Milt & Ethel Bliss, Ethilton Farms, 134 County Hwy. O, Hartford, Wisconsin 53027. Tel.: (414) 474-7258. Open all year. Area 6.*

Ethilton Farms, Wisconsin

THE FARM, 800 acres of timber and dairyland in the heart of Wisconsin's Northwoods, has been in the Palmquist family four generations—since 1898. They promise you "the peace and charm of country life and all the pleasures of wholesome out-door activity." Live in the large farmhouse or guest cottages, and enjoy the best in home-cooked Finnish-American food, a new Finnish sauna and a rustic rec hall with a large stone fireplace. "This warm and hospitable family makes every effort to provide interesting activities for guests," a visitor reports, "from slide shows and farm chores to learning about logging— past and present." Seasonal recreation includes swimming, riding, hayrides, nature trails, cookouts, many games and rugged x-country skiing in winter. Country-style hoe-downs during the summer, with a neighbor playing fiddle. The Palmquists also offer "supervision for children without parents."

□ Accom. 35 guests in rooms & cottages, pvt. & shared baths. Weekly AP: A $145, C $85 (without parent $125). Riding extra. Also MAP rates. 350 mi. NW of Chicago. From Tomahawk (on US 51 & 8) go 18 mi. W. on US 8, ½ mi. N on River Rd. Meet plane in Rhinelander, $10/carload; bus in Tomahawk, $7. *Arthur & Toinie Palmquist, The Farm, Brantwood, Wisconsin 54513. Tel: (715) 564-2558. Open all year. Area 1.*

HAPPY ACRES is a 320-acre dairy farm with cows, chickens, pigs, ducks and horses—"nothing pretentious," reports a visitor, "but so much friendliness—the children in the family are a great asset in hosting guests. Absolutely outstanding meals." Keeping six children and the guests fed means plenty of homemade breads, cakes and pies. Happy Acres adjoins Chequamegon National Forest, where you'll find x-country ski and snowmobile trails, and is near cheese factories, Amish settlements, antiques shops. Weeks at the Bolz's farm start on Sunday and run into Saturday, and they report that "the haymow is the favorite place of old and young alike; and everyone enjoys a hike down the river."

□ Accom. up to 9 guests in 2 dbls. w./shared bath. AP rates: weekly, A $100, C $75; daily, A $18, C $14; incl. riding. 190 mi. NW of Madison—go N on I-90 & US 51 to Wausau, W on Rt. 29 to Abbotsford, N on Rt. 13 to Medford & phone. Meet plane in Mosinee, $20/carload; bus in Medford, no chg. *Conrad & Charlotte Bolz, Happy Acres, Rt. 2, Withee, Wisconsin 54498. Tel.: (715) 785-7539. Open all year. Area 3.*

Harmony Hill Farms, Wisconsin

HARMONY HILL FARMS, in the heart of America's Dairyland, has been in the Schuett family 118 years. It's primarily a dairy farm with grains, corn, alfalfa, 1,100 laying hens and pets. The Schuetts (children 17 and 21) enjoy people and love to see them having a good time, so now that they have a new home they invite vacationers to use the old one—two-story brick. "Our children had experiences they'll never forget because of our hosts' ability to explain, teach and share their love of rural life," observes a guest—experiences that can include milking cows, riding the egg route on Tuesdays, pony and trail rides, maple sugaring in the spring, stacking hay bales, digging spuds or snowmobiling and x-country skiing in winter. Nearby is Rib Mountain State Park.

  ☐ Accom. up to 6 guests in air-cond. floor in farmhouse w./pvt. bath, bedrooms, living room, kitchen. Weekly EP: $125/family. Also daily rates. 280 mi. NW of Chicago—take I-94 & US 51 N thru Wausau, left 3½ mi. on County Hwy. U, right ¾ mi. on 60th Ave. Meet plane in Wausau or Mosinee, train/bus in Wausau, no chg. *Robert & Nathalie Schuett, Harmony Hill Farms, 3000 N. 60th Ave., Wausau, Wisconsin 54401. Tel.: (715) 675-3141. Open all year. Area 4.*

HILLVIEW VACATION HOME is on a 426-acre dairy farm in rolling, scenic crop and timberland near Yellowstone Lake. Having guests is a pleasant hobby for Lillian Wong, a former teacher, who was born here. You'll find good examples of farm enterprises on the property, and of conservation practices—farm ponds, tree planting, wildlife management and contour strip cropping. "It was a refreshing, slow-paced vacation," comments a guest. "Enjoyed participating in the work around

Hillview Vacation Home, Wisconsin

the farm and visiting places like the House on the Rock, Cave of the Mounds, Little Norway and Swiss and Amish communities.''

☐ Ranch-style home w./3 bedrooms sleeps 10, fully equipped except linens. Weekly EP: $150, daily $25, per group. 39 mi. SW of Madison. 150 mi. NW of Chicago—I-90 to Beloit, Rt. 81 W to Argyle, Rt. 78 N 6 mi. to farm. Meet plane/train/bus in Madison, $10/carload. *Lillian V. Wong, Hillview Vacation Home, R. 1, Box 107, Blanchardville, Wisconsin 53516. Tel.: (608) 523-4770. Open all year. Area 5.*

HUNKY DORY FARMS is just what its name implies. Lots of fun activities. Nothing plush, but guests keep coming back for more—35 years in one case, involving four generations of the same family. ''It's an excellent family resort!'' exclaims a frequent visitor. ''The lake is clear and clean, children are welcome, everything is very informal.'' Spring-fed Lake Clare for canoeing, boating, waterskiing, swimming, pontoon rides. You'll also enjoy the new outdoor shuffleboard court at this 640-acre resort, the lawn games, tennis, and hayrides under the stars. You'll sing and laugh around the campfire, join or watch the talent show, fill up at the smorgasbords and family-style meals. Golf nearby. Sunday morning Chapel. Marvel is a registered nurse, should the need arise. No liquor or dogs.

☐ Accom. 100 guests in 22 cottages w./1-3 bedrooms, pvt. baths. Reasonable AP rates—call or write. Also farmhouse, EP rates. 75 mi. N of Minneapolis—take Hwy. 35 N to Rt. 8, E to 1 mi. beyond Rt. 46 turnoff to County Trunk E, go N for 6 mi., right 1 mi., left 1 mi. Meet bus in Amery, no chg. *Alfred & Marvel Nielsen, Hunky Dory Farms, Rt. 1-F, Balsam Lake, Wisconsin 54810. Tel.: (715) 857-5211. Open Apr. 15—Oct. 15. Area 1.*

VACATIONLAND FARM is almost at the tip of the "air-conditioned" peninsula jutting into Lake Michigan in resort-famous Door County. The Kramers grow cherries, hay and grain, and raise horses, cows, goats, deer, pet raccoon, bunnies and more on their 150 acres. "Many families who come here to do sightseeing have a difficult time getting their children to leave the farm," observes Clarissa. Guests call it a "wonderful surrounding for children and adults alike," with horseback trail rides, surrey and pony rides. Excellent food at the farm restaurant and interesting gifts at its Iron Horse shop.

  □ Accom. 34 guests in 9 air-cond. units w./pvt. baths. Daily EP: $18–$30 for 2, $3 ea. addl., incl. limited riding. Meals at farm's restaurant. 170 mi. N of Milwaukee—take Hwy. 57 N to ½ mi. S of Sister Bay. Meet bus in Sister Bay, no chg. *Willard & Clarissa Kramer, Vacationland Farm, Sister Bay, Wisconsin 54234. Tel.: (414) 854-2525. Open May 15 thru Oct. Area 4.*

Wyoming

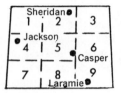

The Tetons, their peaks etching a sharp, jagged horizon, rise so abruptly from rolling range country and flowering meadows that they seem more like a stage backdrop than the real thing. In this northwest corner of the state, Grand Teton National Park and Yellowstone National Park provide enough grandeur to last one a lifetime—though the state's beauty is not confined to this area. Wyoming became a state in 1890. Explorers, trappers, traders, pioneers and finally Texas cattlemen settled here in the 1800s. Rodeos and the cowboy are a very real part of Wyoming today, where a quaint law requires all store owners to provide hitching posts for horses.

BILL CODY'S RANCH INN, a rambling log lodge and cabins snuggled in a narrow, pine-shaded canyon at 6,200 feet, is hosted by Buffalo Bill's grandson, Bill Cody, and his wife, Barbara. "Bill Cody is part of the Old West and has a wealth of knowledge which he shares with guests," one writes. "They are concerned and friendly hosts—one of the most congenial and interesting places we have visited." They'll take you on daily trail rides into the Absaroka Wilderness in the Shoshone National Forest, and there will be cookouts, square dances, campfires and sing-alongs as well as "solid ranch-style fare at mealtime with five dinners to choose from each night." Off the ranch: whitewater float trips, fishing and exploring historic old Cody (the town).

☐ Accom. 60 guests in units that vary in size. Daily AP: $38–$60/person; under 5 yrs., $15. Daily EP: $24–$45/unit, riding extra; no kitchen facilities, no meals at ranch, on EP rates. 120 mi. SW of Billings. 25 mi. W of Cody on US 16. Meet plane/train/bus in Cody, no chg. for AP guests. Other points, reas. chg. *Bill & Barbara Cody, Bill Cody's Ranch Inn, P.O. Box 1390-R, Cody, Wyoming 82414. Tel.: (307) 587-2097. Open May thru Sep. & Dec. 15–Mar. 15. Area 1.*

CASTLE ROCK RANCH, hosted by Joe and Ally Tilden (still in their twenties), occupies 2,600 acres with hay and cattle, sage and scrub flats, hills and tree-filled mountains and two miles of river frontage. They pamper their guests with baby sitters, cabin girls for clean-up, good ranch-style meals ("plus perpetual snacks") and unlimited riding, trout fishing, pool or river swimming, hiking, games, a sauna and day trips to Yellowstone. "Really enjoyed it," declares a guest. "Our children were anxious to stay longer. The hosts are very accomodating. We had excellent meals at the main lodge, and a very comfortable cabin." You're welcome to bring your pets, and to enjoy such local attractions as Shoshone River float trips, Cody Nite Rodeo, Old Trail Town, and the Buffalo Bill Historical Center—"A must!"

□ Accom. 24 guests in 8 cabins varying in size, pvt. baths. Daily AP: A $34–$50, ea. addl. $30–$47, C discts.—8–11 yrs. 12%, 5–7 20%, 1–4 50%. Riding incl. 21 mi. SW of Cody—follow signs on South Fork Rd. (Rt. 291). Meet plane/train/bus in Billings, $75/carload, or in Cody, no chg. *Joe & Ally Tilden, Castle Rock Ranch, R. R. 2, Box 3700-FR, Cody, Wyoming 82414. Tel.: (307) 587-2076. Open May 15–Nov. 15. Area 1.*

CROSS MILLIRON RANCH in the green Wind River valley is surrounded by spectacular scenery. On this 5,000-acre ranch at 6,000 feet elevation, the Millers match novice and expert riders to their well-mannered horses and give excellent instruction. "Our hosts displayed a unique warmth and kindness," stresses a guest. "We learned about Indians, irrigation, animal care, rocks and fossils. The overnight pack trip in silent wilderness was fascinating." Horseback games and a rip-snorting rodeo right on the ranch are weekly highlights. It's a family operation, with good fishing, rock hunting and wilderness adventure in addition to riding.

□ Accom. 30 guests in 10 cabins & bunkhouse, pvt. baths. Weekly AP: A $200, C to 10 yrs. $160 (under 3 free), incl. riding & guides. 177 mi. W of Casper, 5 mi. W of Burris, on US 26. Meet plane in Riverton or bus in Shoshoni, $20/carload. *Larry & Connie Miller, Cross Milliron Ranch, Crowheart, Wyoming 82512. Tel.: (307) 486-2279. Open Jun.–Sep. Area 4.*

Castle Rock Ranch, Wyoming

CROSSED SABRES RANCH, at 7,000 feet in the evergreen Shoshone National Forest near Yellowstone, offers spacious log cabins and lodge, and trail rides into the Absaroka Range—"the most beautiful mountains in the world," claimed Teddy Roosevelt. Here you'll find clean air and pure spring water, and you'll be waited upon by an experienced, jovial and entertaining staff. Barbecues on Sunday and movies Monday night. On Tuesday you go in to Cody for the rodeo and museum and a picnic. An overnight pack trip, square dance, van trip through Yellowstone, steak fry, corral games, Shoshone River float trip and a staff show round out the week. "It was like taking the kids to camp and getting to stay yourself," explains a guest. Babysitters give adults a chance to ride or catch cutthroat trout with no worries for the kids.

☐ Accom. up to 60 guests in 18 cabins for 1-8, pvt. baths. Weekly AP: A $275, C 7-17 yrs. $225, 1-6 $150, incl. riding. 43 mi. W of Cody, 9 mi. E of Yellowstone, ¼ mi. off US 16. Meet plane/bus in Cody, no chg. *Rich & Donna Marta, Crossed Sabres Ranch, Box F, Wapiti, Wyoming 82450. Tel.: (307) 587-3750. Open Jun.-Aug. Area 1.*

DEER FORKS RANCH is a 5,900-acre working cattle spread "at the end of the road, three miles from our nearest neighbors," report the Middletons. This means plenty of quiet and solitude, along with real ranch work. "We loved it," exclaims a guest. "We rounded up cows, repaired fences, stacked bales of hay, separated steers from heifers, helped the vet do pregnancy tests and rode superbly trained horses." You can do the same, and enjoy fresh garden produce and home baking in the bargain, along with the Middletons and their 2 children (5 and 8). Fish for trout, take in rodeos and livestock auctions, go birding, hunt Indian relics.

☐ Rustic & new log cabins, pvt. baths, for 12 guests, & trailer hookup. AP rates: weekly, A $130, C to 10 yrs., $95; daily, A $19, C $14. Also EP rates. Riding extra. 75 mi. SE of Casper. At Douglas exit on I-25 go 10½ mi. on Esterbrook secondary, right 14 mi. on Rd. #4 (take all left turns). Meet plane in Casper, $35/carload, bus in Douglas, $15. *Ben & Pauli Middleton, Deer Forks Ranch, Rt. 6, Douglas, Wyoming 82633. Tel.: (307) 358-2033. Open all year. Area 6.*

DIAMOND SEVEN BAR RANCH in the Black Hills is a 6,000-acre cattle ranch. One or two families at a time stay with the Mahoneys (children 12, 9 and 3) in their new home and cabin in this lovely valley. They all love riding but give you plenty of freedom to spend your vacation as you like. "If you don't enjoy the Diamond Seven Bar, you'd probably find fault with heaven," remarks an enthusiastic guest. Ride, fish, hike, help with the ranch work or just loaf and watch the deer and the butterflies. Hearty meals feature home baking and organic garden produce. Close at hand are Devils Tower, sawmills, a lookout tower. The Mahoneys prefer non-drinkers; also non-smokers, but no hard and fast rule.

Crossed Sabres Ranch, Wyoming

☐ Accom. 1 or 2 families in 2 rooms w./bath, & cabin w./2 bedrooms, living room, privy. Weekly AP: A $140, C $70 (under 4 yrs. free). Weekly EP: $70 ea. for 1 or 2, $25 ea. addl. Riding incl. 90 mi. W of Rapid City (South Dakota)—from Belle Fourche, W on Rts. 34 & 24 to Alva, at Post Office 3 mi. S on dirt rd. Meet plane in Rapid City, $20/carload, bus in Belle Fourche, $8. *Gerald & Betsy Mahoney, Diamond Seven Bar Ranch, Alva, Wyoming 82711. Tel.: (307) 467-5612. Open Dec. thru Oct. Area 3.*

FIR CREEK RANCH is run by Peter and Gretchen Finch and their five children (11 to 23)—"very special people who make you feel at home, like members of their family," as a guest describes them. Their beautiful ranch on the Buffalo Fork of the Snake River is near Grand Teton National Park and Jackson Hole. Join them in ranch activities, all-day cookout rides, pack trips, float trips (extra), fishing and ranch-style food with home-baked bread. They grow hay, and feed 300 head of cattle and 30 horses. "It was the highlight of our trip through the west," points out a visitor. "It's like one big family here." You're apt to see elk, moose and deer. In winter, there's guided x-country skiing for wildlife viewing. The Finches are active in church and community affairs.

☐ Dbls. in main lodge w./pvt. baths for 12 guests. Daily AP: $25–$28, C 1–7 yrs. less, riding extra. 43 mi. N of Jackson—go 3.5 mi. E of Moran on US 26, 3.5 mi. N on Buffalo Valley Rd. to sign. Meet plane/bus in Jackson, no chg.; train in Rock Springs, $50/carload. *Peter & Gretchen Finch, Fir Creek Ranch, Moran, Wyoming 83013. Tel.: (307) 543-2416. Open all year exc. Christmas. Area 1.*

FLYING V RANCH borders Grand Teton National Park and Teton National Forest. The Gros Ventre River, with cutthroat and rainbow trout, flows through it. It's a place to enjoy the striking view of the Teton peaks, the birds, beaver and wild-flowers and the peace and beauty of the ranch. "Trail boss" Roy guides riders on spectacular forest trails, and Becky's kitchen turns out some of the best dishes in Jackson Hole Country. Their teenagers are active in whatever is going on—cookouts, hikes, visits to Teton Park and evenings around the open fire. "Fine hospitality, splendid food and magnificent scenery," comments a guest. "The Chambers deliver what they lead you to expect."

☐ 4 duplex cabins, pvt. baths, for 20 guests. Weekly AP: $225–$250/person, 1–3 yrs. free. Riding incl. 18 mi. NE of

Jackson on the Gros Ventre Rd. Meet plane/bus in Jackson, no chg. *Roy & Becky Chambers, Flying V Ranch, Box 575, Kelly P.O., Jackson Hole, Wyoming 83011. Tel.: (307) 733-2799. Open Jun.–Sep. Area 4.*

[handwritten annotations: "1/3 Dep down", "d 50 adult $35 a day   10 c under   make reservation   as soon as possible"]

GOOSEWING RANCH in Gros Ventre country near Jackson Hole and Grand Teton National Park is "a place to experience the friendliness of the West" as one guest describes it. "You feel like a great big family." Congeniality, meals and relaxation center at the spacious log lodge and the heated pool, and guests are housed in attractive log cabins—"roughing it in comfort" is the hosts' modest appraisal. There's no regimentation, but a competent wrangler guides trail riders, matching them to gentle or spirited horses. There is splendid trout fishing—"the four of us brought back 24 30-inch cutthroat trout," a guest reports. Fossils, wildflowers, blue heron and mountain beauty await the hiker and naturalist. In winter it's a 45-minute snowmobile ride in to the ranch; unlimited riding and ski touring.

☐ Accom. 20 guests in 8 cabins, pvt. baths. Daily AP: $35/person, 1–3 yrs. free, incl riding. 30 mi. E of Jackson airport. Meet plane/bus in Jackson, no chg. *Harold & Claudette Shervin, Goosewing Ranch, P.O. Box 496-F, Jackson, Wyoming 83001. Tel.: (307) 733-2768. Open all but Dec. Area 4.*

GRIZZLY RANCH, between Cody and Yellowstone National Park, is geared for weeklong guests who love to ride—breakfast rides, morning and afternoon rides, daylong rides. Tree-shaded log guest cabins are along the creek, and meals at the main lodge ("outstanding" writes a guest) are family-style. "We raise horses, mules and hay," notes Rick, a former rodeo bareback rider, "and we plan each day's activities for whatever appeals to our guests—we want them to feel at home." There's a stocked pond in front of the lodge for children and casting, and it's a half mile to the Shoshone River for excellent trout. The tennis court doubles for volleyball and square dances. With unlimited access to wilderness trails, pack trips (up to 7 days) are a specialty. Nearby: Cody's many activities, and Yellowstone.

☐ Accom. 15 guests in 4 cabins, pvt. baths. Weekly AP: from $315 for 1, to $245 ea. for 5, incl. riding, Cody rodeo, river float. Pack trip $70/day. 26 mi. W of Cody & E of Yellowstone, on US 14-16-20. Meet plane/train in Billings (Montana), $50/carload; pickup in Cody, no chg. *Rick & Candy Felts, Grizzly Ranch, North Fork Rt. F, Cody, Wyoming 82414. Tel.: (307) 587-3966. Open Jun. thru Sep. Area 1.*

HIDDEN VALLEY RANCH covers 4,000 acres in a strikingly beautiful valley where Hereford cattle graze, with mountains on three sides. Gourmet meals at its Supper Club are popular with Cody residents as well as ranch guests. Attractive cabins feature wall-to-wall carpeting, western paintings and authentic Indian artifacts. You'll swim in a heated pool, play tennis, catch trout in the stream, and you can go on cookouts, trail rides and scenic trips. On weeklong visits rates include the Cody rodeo, a float trip on the Shoshone River, and visits to the Buffalo Bill Museum and Yellowstone National Park. Trout fishing in both stream and lake: "We enjoyed the horseback riding mostly to out-of-the-way places—not just the usual trail rides," notes a guest. Pack trips into Yellowstone, Absaroka and Teton Wilderness can be arranged.

☐ Accom. 25 guests in lodge & cabins w./elec. heat & pvt. baths. Daily AP: A $45, C $40; EP, $26 for 2, $3.50 ea. addl., infants free. Riding incl. in AP rates. Pack trips extra. 15 mi. SW of Cody—go 1 mi. W on Rt. 16, 9 mi. S on Southfork Rd., turn off SW, cross bridge, go 3½ mi., gravel rd. 1 mi. Meet plane/bus in Cody, no chg., train in Billings, $50/carload. *Marge Poulsen Bohl, Hidden Valley Ranch, Rt. 2, Box 3650, Cody, Wyoming 82414. Tel.: (307) 587-5090. Open May thru Oct. Area 1.*

LOST CREEK RANCH borders Grand Teton National Park in a most scenic area of Jackson Hole Country, near the Snake River. There is a horse for each guest, and hundreds of miles of trails for riding or hiking interlace the valley and mountain passes. Expert guides lead pack trips deep into the wilderness, with some of the best trout fishing in the U.S. Guests live in two-bedroom cabins, many with two baths, living room, open fireplace, private porch. The spacious living room and attractive dining room at the Lodge are favorite gathering spots, as are the tennis court and heated pool. There's also a children's den and adults' card room. "We specialize in excellent food served family-style," say the hosts, "and can cater to special diets with advance notice."

☐ Accom. 45 guests in 18 cabins, pvt. baths. Weekly AP: $308–$644/person, discts. for non-riders & children under 6. (Oct.–Mar., housekeeping cabins by special request.) 25 mi. NE of Jackson; meet guests in Jackson, no chg. *Lost Creek Ranch, P.O. Box 95, Moose, Wyoming 83012. Tel.: (307) 733-3435. Open May thru Sep. (Other months on request.) Area 4.*

MEDICINE BOW LODGE AND GUEST RANCH, at 8,000 feet in scenic Medicine Bow National Forest, is geared for families. The warm and capable hosts have two small children, and counselors plan riding, hiking and games for kids, and all-day hot dog rides. Easy or difficult trails for adults, and for them it's an all-day wine-and-cheese ride. There's much to do—lake and stream fishing, an overnight pack trip, a weekly rodeo (everyone participates), square dances, songfests or just loafing—and in winter, snowmobiling, x-country skiing and snowshoeing. Cozy, unsophisticated log cabins for guests, good hearty meals at the lodge.

☐ Accom. 25-30 guests in 8 pvt. cabins w./baths. Weekly AP: A $223–$256, C $103–$187; daily rates; riding incl. Off-season 10% less. Pack trip, $22. 22 mi. SE of Saratoga; 50 mi. W of Laramie on Rt. 130. Meet plane/train/bus in Laramie or Rawlins, $15/carload ($25/carload in winter if pass closed). *John & Teri Owens, Medicine Bow Lodge and Guest Ranch, Box 752-V, Saratoga, Wyoming 82331. Tel.: (307) 326-5439. Open all year. Area 8.*

PELLATZ RANCH is 8,000 acres of wide-open space on which Don and Betty and their four teenagers raise sheep and cattle.

Pellatz Ranch, Wyoming

"Join us in ranch activities if you wish," they suggest. Or you can spend your days riding, hiking and swimming in the pool. Cookouts are a regular feature, and long-term guests are treated to overnight camping in the Black Hills. "Fantastic people, great food—home-grown and home-baked," advises a guest. Fossils and petrified wood and plenty of wildlife await amateur naturalists, and there are local rodeos. Non-smokers and non-drinkers preferred.

☐ Accom. 2 families in rooms & guest house, shared baths. Weeky AP: A $125, C $100, incl. riding. 102 mi. NE of Casper, 48 mi. N of Douglas. From Douglas exit on I-25, go 35 mi. N on Hwy. 59 to Bill, 6 mi. N on dirt rd., 6 mi. E to ranch. Meet plane in Casper, $30/carload. *Don & Betty Pellatz, Pellatz Ranch, Rt. 2, Douglas, Wyoming 82633. Tel.: (307) 358-2380. Open all year. Area 6.*

7-D Ranch, Wyoming

RIMROCK DUDE RANCH has been known for its real down-on-the-ranch hospitality since 1927. Wilderness pack trips are part of it, along with watching wranglers from the corral fence. "Beautiful trails behind the ranch lead to passes at 10,000 feet," says Glenn Fales, who had shoes on 100 horses last summer. He recommends choice spots at timberline for sleeping out, seeing wildlife and catching trout. "Outstanding hosts, hospitality, cabins and area," notes a guest. There's square dancing, lots of riding, ranch-style meals and a rec hall to keep everyone happy at the ranch—or take in the rodeo and museum and a float trip in Cody, and visit Yellowstone—all of which are provided. Or come for a week's pack trip.

☐ Accom. 35 guests in attractive heated cabins for 1–8, pvt. baths, some w./fireplace & living room. Weekly AP: $147–$329, incl. riding, overnight pack & float trip. 7-day pack trip, $450. 26 mi. E of Yellowstone & W of Cody—1 mi. off US 14-16-20. Meet plane/train/bus in Cody, no chg., Billings, $60/carload. *Glenn & Alice Fales, & Gary, Rimrock Dude Ranch, Northfolk Rt. Box FS, Cody, Wyoming 82414. Tel.: (307) 587-3970. Open Jun.-Aug. Area 1.*

7-D RANCH, in the spectacular Sunlight Basin, is where the Dominicks show guests "some of the most beautiful country in the world and offer quality riding, quality food and quality service." With 55 riding horses they take guests on breakfast or all-day rides, supper-and-sunset rides, and pack trips into the high wilderness of Shoshone National Forest. Sunlight Creek runs for a mile through the ranch with "some of the best trout fishing anywhere," and alpine lakes at 10,000 feet provide golden trout. A guest sums it up as "simply magnificent country, delightful hosts and crew, and an incredibly good experience for our family." Hiking, climbing and swimming round out the activities, along with gymkhanas, trapshooting, softball, square dances, and a visit to Cody's Rodeo and Whitney Gallery of Western Art. The rec room and attractive lodge are home-base for less energetic reading or impromptu fun. Hosts' children are 9 and 11.

☐ 10 log cabins, pvt. baths, accom. 36 guests. Daily AP: $36–$48 ($31–$43, Jun. & Sep.), incl. riding & most activities. Pack trip, $85–$100/day. 120 mi. S of Billings; 55 mi. NW of Cody—N on Rt. 120, left on Rt. 296, left on Sunlight Basin Rd. Meet plane in Cody, $50/vanload, or Billings (Montana), $75. *John and Lynn Dominick, 7-D Ranch, Box 109-A, Cody, Wyoming 82414. Tel.: (307) 587-2686 or 3997. Open Jun.-Sep. Area 1.*

SHOSHONE LODGE is just four miles from the east entrance to Yellowstone National Park, high in the Absaroka Range of the Rockies. Started in 1924 by Keith's grandfather, the Lodge has been host to three generations of guests. "We offer that old-fashioned, unstructured, restful vacation," Keith declares. This includes "delicious, home-cooked meals and fresh-baked breads" in the spacious dining room of the native log lodge, where a friendly lounge with big open fires is a favorite gathering place. You can ride horseback, fish, hike or arrange a wilderness pack trip. Various outdoor games at the Lodge, children's playground, coin laundry, sundries. Area activities include rodeos, river float trips, cookouts, square dances and visits to Yellowstone or Cody.

☐ Accom. 50 guests in 16 log cabins among the pines, 1–3 bedrooms, pvt. baths; 3 housekeeping units. Daily EP: sgl. cabin, $20–$22; dbl., $22–$28; ea. addl., $4. Riding extra. 48 mi. W of Cody on US 14-16-20; meet plane/bus, no chg. *Keith Dahlem, Shoshone Lodge, P.O. Box 960, Cody, Wyoming 82414. Tel.: (307) 587-4044. Open mid-May thru Oct. Area 1.*

TOGWOTEE MOUNTAIN LODGE, nestled among the pines at the base of Mt. Angle, specializes in friendly atmosphere, hiking trails, trout fishing and a playground with miniature log cabin for the "little people," and a restaurant with fine food. There are dinner cookouts on horseback, trail rides, and overnight pack trips into the Teton Wilderness for fishermen, photographers, rock hounds or anyone else. Float trips on the Snake River. Grand Teton and Yellowstone National Parks and Jackson Hole are within 50 miles. For Nordic skiers: miles of groomed trails—campfires and hot apple cider on moonlight tours. For snowmobilers: rentals, trails, and a 150-mile, 6-day guided tour, the "Togwotee Trek," involving four lodges and spectacular terrain.

☐ Rooms in Lodge, pvt. baths, for 75 guests. Daily EP: $20–$26/dbl. room, $18/sgl., rollaways or cribs, $3; camper parking, $4. Special activities extra. Also weekly rates. 70 mi. NE of Jackson Hole, 38 mi. NW of Dubois; on US 26/287. Meet plane/bus in Jackson, $5/person. *Dave & Judie Helgeson, Togwotee Mountain Lodge, Box 91-D, Moran, Wyoming 83013. Tel.: (307) 543-2847. Open all but May. Area 4.*

VALLEY RANCH was homesteaded in 1892, one of the oldest guest ranches in the West, and the old-time charm and tradition have not been lost in the renovations that have taken place through the years. It's also a working ranch with cattle, pigs, chickens and other animals. Oak (a Ph.D.) is a biologist and professional photographer. Ranch activities emphasize nature walks, birding, geology, fossil hunting and wildflower study as well as trout fishing, hiking and excellent riding with horses for experts and beginners. Wilderness trail rides and pack trips are a specialty. The scenic glacial valley is surrounded by spectacular peaks of the Washakie Wilderness Area in the Shoshone National Forest. Arts and crafts, square dances, photography, mu-

Valley Ranch, Wyoming

Bill Cody's Ranch Inn, Wyoming

sic, campfire sings, hayrides and cookouts are among the other activities. "A great spot for families," say the guests.

☐ 26 cabins w./woodstoves & pvt. baths, accom. 45 guests. Weekly AP: Jul.–Aug., A $304 average, C 10%-25% disct.; less spring & fall. Riding incl. 40 mi. S of Cody—go 39 mi. on South Fork Rd. (Rt. 291), 1 mi. on ranch rd. Meet plane/bus in Cody, no chg. *Oak & Lisa Thorne, Valley Ranch, South Fork Star Rt. V, Cody, Wyoming 82414. Tel.: (307) 587-4661. Open May thru Oct. Area 1. (See Chapter, "For Teens and Under.")*

WHISTLE CREEK RANCH *looks* like a real cattle ranch, and it is. Walt and Betty raise beef cattle, pinto horses, hay, grain and corn in this irrigated, desert country of the Big Horn Basin. And they make guests welcome in the antiques-filled ranch house, attractive log cabins, and at family-style, good wholesome meals. "Riding is what a vacation at Whistle Creek is all about," comments a guest. The Sternes ride from early spring until the snow flies. Get instruction in horsemanship and roping, or learn to check fences, pitch hay and handle ranch chores. You can join roundups and make an overnight trip to "cow camp," swim in Whistle Creek, visit the Cody Nite Rodeo, and take in other sights of this scenic area.

   ☐ Accom. 20 guests, mostly pvt. baths. Weekly AP: sgl. room, $235; dbl., $215 ea.; C under 6 yrs., 50% less. Daily rates. Riding incl. 37 mi. NE of Cody; 12 mi. SW of Lovell—S off Hwy. 14A, 12 mi. S on Rt. 32. Meet plane in Cody, $10/person, or in Billings (Montana), $20; bus in Lovell, no chg. *Walt & Betty Sterne, Whistle Creek Ranch, P.O. Box 752-A, Lovell, Wyoming 82431. Tel.: (307) 548-2478. Open all year. Area 2.*

ZIMMERSCHIED RANCH is for those who want to visit a real working cattle ranch and be treated like one of the family. Roam and ride on 9,100 acres. Help with ranch chores, swim, fish or visit Yellowstone, the Black Hills and the Badlands. "The entire ranch was ours to explore," remarks a visitor. "They are fantastically kind, warm people, with fine horses, simple accommodations and wonderful cooking." The Z's raise their own meat, make jellies from wild fruit, bake bread, churn butter, make ice cream. The scenic area includes the Devils Tower.

   ☐ Accom. 2 families & 4 under-16-yr.-olds in 2 trailers and ranch house rooms. Weekly AP: A $150, C $90 (to 3 yrs. free), incl. riding. 163 mi. E of Sheridan—go 135 mi. E on I-90 to Moorcroft, 24 mi. N on Hwy. 14, right 4 mi. after bridge. Meet plane in Rapid City, $10/carload; bus in Moorcroft, no chg. *Art & Julia Zimmerschied, Zimmerschied 33 Ranch, Moorcroft, Wyoming 82721. Tel.: (307) 756-3205. Open Jun. thru Aug. Area 3.*

Zimmerschied Ranch, Wyoming

Virgin Islands

With a temperature that varies between 70° and
90° and located about 40 miles east of Puerto
Rico, the United States Virgin Islands are part
of the Antilles chain that separates the Atlantic
Ocean from the Caribbean Sea. St. Croix, with
84 square miles of mostly cultivated land, was
known as "the garden of the West Indies" by
the Danes. The island was discovered by Chris-
topher Columbus in 1493, colonized by the English and Dutch 150 years later, and subse-
quently taken over by the Spanish, then the
French, Knights of Malta and Denmark—from
whom it was bought in 1917 by the United
States. Today it is a holiday mecca year 'round,
but especially during winter months.

SPRAT HALL PLANTATION is a "tropical beach resort with
many water activities—and gourmet meals of tropical fruits and
vegetables and fresh caught seafood" as described by Jim Hurd.
It also sounds much like a ranch—200 acres, crops and a riding
stables with 30 riding horses. But at this "ranch" the riding
trails lead through rain forests, crops consist of tropical fruits,
swimming is in crystal clear Caribbean waters at a white coral
sand beach with restaurant and bar, shaded by coconut trees,
and the horses have debuted in a Burt Lancaster movie. The
plantation Great House (oldest on the island, dating from
French Occupation of 1650-1690), Slave Quarters and Cottages
provide guest rooms and housekeeping units—"well-appointed
and very comfortable," says a guest, returning for a "relaxing,
casual and terrific" week.

☐ Accom. for 50 guests, all w./pvt. baths, most air-cond.
Daily EP, Dec. 16-Apr. 15: rooms $56 for 2, $67 for 3; cottages
$65 for 2, $100 for 4. Off season rates. Riding, waterskiing,
sailing, deep sea fishing, extra. 1 mi. N of Frederiksted. *Jim &
Joyce Hurd, Sprat Hall Plantation, P.O. Box 695-F,
Frederiksted, St. Croix, Virgin Islands 00840. Tel.: (809) 772-
0305. Open all year.*

Camp Chaparral, Texas

For Teens and Under

This book has always called attention to rural hosts who invite children and young teens to visit them and fit into the events of life on the farm or ranch like a member of the family. The Appendix on page 207 refers to the coverage of these places in earlier sections of the book.

But this chapter, if you are teenage or under, is especially for you. It tells about some adventurous, purposeful experiences that can give you skills and perceptions which you'll value the rest of your life.

Many of these vacation ideas have been developed, as one rancher puts it, "for kids caught up in the city-suburban life who need a chance to live close to nature and really accomplish something." It's like having a holiday and getting a headstart at the same time—a headstart in knowing a lot more about yourself and others and the world you live in.

What better way to learn about the world, for example, than from the seat of a 10-speed bike. If you have one, you can wheel with companions on trips both here and abroad that are "physically and emotionally demanding"—but they're also enlightening and fun.

Then there's the world you discover living on a farm. It can be an intensive rural experience "particularly well suited for bright, motivated teenagers who wish to expand their horizons," one parent advises. Taking responsibility for farm animals, tending and harvesting a garden, and plowing, planting, cultivating and reaping crops, clearing weeds and trees out of a spring-fed pond to make it good for swimming—these are achievements that give you a feeling of satisfaction and an idea of what farming is all about.

For children as well as teens, a ranch or farm vacation is really enlightening. So much goes on. If you're there as a member of the family you may get involved, for instance, in helping to bring in the hay, gathering vegetables, mending fences, watching the birth of a calf, catching trout and cooking them, going swimming and even helping with a cattle roundup—once you've learned to ride a horse.

Horsemanship, in fact, has many aspects. The experiences recommended here provide everything from basic riding instruction to the thrill and competition of gymkhanas, horse shows or roping, barrel racing, pole bending and other rodeo skills.

Riding and learning to take care of your horse is a specialty, of course, at ranch camps. But a camp program is apt to offer much more, such as how to milk a cow or goat, or how to go crawfishing or crabbing or paddle a pirogue (a hollowed log canoe), how to identify plants and birds in different life zones, how to pack a horse for a wilderness trek and how to camp out. Camping is one thing at a campground with the family car, but quite different when you're canoeing, kayaking, backpacking or riding a horse into the wilderness.

Like camping, most of the experiences described in this chapter are anything but deluxe. A rustic bunkhouse—or a sleeping bag on an outdoor platform, in a tent or under a tree— may be your shelter from the elements. And in some of these programs a lot of hard work mixes with the fun. There's no pampering, but the instruction and supervision you need are always there, and the fun of achievement makes the work worthwhile.

Also worthwhile is the fact that when you're planning, working and accomplishing something together, affection and respect for one another develop. It's usually with mixed feelings that you see the experience coming to an end. So whatever vacation experience you choose, dig in, get really involved and enjoy it!

Arizona

PRICE CANYON RANCH offers a two-week program for kids 8 years old and up (including adults) who would like to learn how to ride and care for horses while living on a hard-working cattle ranch. Scotty Anderson has a naturalist's wealth of knowledge and love for the plants, birds and animals in all five life-zones, from 4,400 to 9,900 feet, on this beautiful ranch. You'll assist with the branding, help round up cattle, move them from one pasture to another and leave feed for them in the mountains. And you'll observe record-keeping at Scotty's weather station and go on a mountain camping trip. Learning is fun in surroundings like these, even for your hosts. "Our young guests provide us with plenty of heartwarming experiences," Scotty says. (Ranch listed also in "Arizona" section.)

☐ $200 for 2 weeks incl. complete program. Meet plane/bus in Tucson, $65/carload; in Douglas, no chg. *Scotty & Alice Anderson, Price Canyon Ranch, P.O. Box 1065, Douglas, Arizona 85607. Tel.: (602) 558-2383.*

California

CHOLAME CREEK RANCH is a place to learn horsemanship, and from June through August it's for 8- to-16-year-olds. (Families and adults other months—see "California" section.) Both Gloria and Martin come from long-time ranching families, and their 5,000-acre ranch was homesteaded generations back by their families. "The children are learning all the time," Gloria explains, "with activities centered around horses. First they learn to care for them and gain confidence, then go trail riding, have gymkhanas (games on horseback) and work cattle." They also go on hikes, study wildlife and nature lore and sing around evening bonfires. On an optional 80-mile trek to the beach in August they ride and camp out. Good supervision and a staff of clean, wholesome young people is emphasized.

☐ Camp sessions, Jun. thru Aug., min. 2 weeks, $350. Also 8-day spring sessions for children. 200 mi. N of Los Angeles near Paso Robles. *Martin & Gloria Van Horn, Cholame Creek Ranch, P.O. Box 8-R, Cholame, California 93431. Tel.: (805) 463-2320.*

Cholame Creek Ranch, California

Cholame Creek Ranch, California

NEW PIONEER RANCH & SUMMER CAMP is where Bob and Jan Hooper (former teachers) and their children (7,11 and 14) share "pioneering" with 6- to 17-year-olds. They raise their own meat and organic vegetables, have goats (for milk) and chickens, make ice cream, butter and cheese, grind wheat, bake bread and spin wool. Campers do a pioneer's share of the farm chores like milking a goat or cow or bucking hay, and they ride horseback, hike, fish for trout, swim, canoe and pan for gold. They live in old and weathered buildings, use an old-fashioned outhouse and sleep on an outdoor platform—and love it. Some stay on in winter and attend local schools. The key to the camp's success? "My kids are good campers and like animals and the outdoor life, and they love the Hoopers and Jan's cookery," a parent explains.

☐ Camp sessions, Jul. & Aug., 3 weeks, $465. Other months, weekly AP: families, A $140, C $100; C alone, $450/month. 80 mi. W of Redding, 300 mi. N of San Francisco—go N on I-5 to Hwy. 299, W to Douglas City, S on Hwy. 3 to 9 mi. past Hayfork, left on 13 Dips Rd. Meet plane/bus in Redding, $30. *Bob & Jan Hooper, New Pioneer Ranch & Summer Camp, P.O. Box 969-F, Hayfork, California 96041. Tel.: (916) 628-5196.*

Idaho

DIAMOND T RANCH is in scenic northern Idaho where the Lewises share with 15- to 19-year-olds the experience of developing their ranch. You'll live in a loft above the horse stalls in the redwood barn, help cut and haul trees to build cabins, then move into them. And you'll clear out weeds and trees to make spring-fed ponds good for swimming and for trout. Early campers will help plant oats, alfalfa and a vegetable garden for later arrivals to harvest. Former teachers and counselors in Aspen, and having grown up on ranches, the Lewises want kids who have been caught up in the city-suburban life "to have a chance to really accomplish something—to live a family life close to nature and to animals—to walk through trees, fish a little, find themselves." It's a chance to gain real insight into ranch life with outstanding, dedicated hosts who are loved and respected for their straightforward dealings with young people.

☐ Sessions for 20 campers begin mid-Jun. & late-Jul., 5 weeks, $800. Meet kids at Spokane airport or Amtrak to Sandpoint. *Byron & Myra Lewis, Diamond T Ranch, Box 625 HCR, Clark Fork, Idaho 83811. Tel.: (208) 266-1186.*

Illinois

WHITE PINES RANCH on 500 scenic acres with horses and cattle, gives 8- to 18-year-old "ranch hands" a chance to live, work and play, western style, all through July and August. "Activities start the second you get up," reports a young rancher, "and last to the second you go to bed. The thing you enjoy the most is riding the horses, 'cause after all it's a dude ranch." But you also enjoy the heated outdoor pool, crafts, volleyball, archery, baseball, hayrides, moonlight trail rides and singing 'round the campfire. Buildings are winterized, and from September through June the ranch is open weekends to groups— scout, church, school and other youth groups—who bring their own counselors. In winter it's skiing, tobogganing, snowmobiling and sledding in addition to horseback riding.

☐ Dorm accom. for 200 guests. Jul.–Aug., ranch-camp, $150/week (Sun. p.m.–Sat. noon); $35/addl. day. Groups, Sep.–Jun., Fri. p.m.–Sun. p.m.: $50/person ($40 Dec.–Feb.). 100 mi. W of Chicago—Rt. 64 W to Oregon, left on Rt. 2, right on Pines Rd. for 4 mi. Meet plane/bus in Oregon or Dixon, no chg. *Dick & Dee Little, White Pines Ranch, Pines Rd., Oregon, Illinois 61061. Tel.: (815) 732-7923.*

Louisiana

ACADIAN SUMMER CAMP is in the heart of Louisiana's Cajun (Acadian-French descent) land. It offers a taste of old-fashioned Cajun country life plus other activities for boys and girls 7 to 17 on its 95 rolling prairie acres where an authentic Acadian cottage serves as camp headquarters. Crawfishing, crabbing, animal care, quilting and making cornhusk dolls and Acadian sunbonnets provide new experiences for campers, who also learn to churn butter and make ice cream, and ride in buggies and wagons and a pirogue—a hollowed log canoe. All the traditional activities, too—horseback riding, softball, tennis, tumbling, riflery, carpentry, cookouts, ceramics and plaster, swimming and more—and tutoring in reading, English and math if it's needed. "Activities are well supervised," writes a parent, "and the children help to plan them. I was impressed with the attention given my child." Campers live in an air-conditioned bunkhouse.

☐ Weekly camp, Jun. 10–Aug. 11, $125/week, $110/addl. week. Tutoring, $25/week. 55 mi. W of Baton Rouge, 15 mi. N of Lafayette. *Richard S. & Wanda Morgan, Acadian Summer Camp, Rt. 1, Box 19, Sunset, Louisiana 70584. Tel.: (318) 662-3379.*

OPEN ROAD EXPERIENCES combines camping, wilderness skills and touring into a program that has ten boys from the 6th to 9th grades journeying from New Orleans to New England and Canada and back on a 7-week summer trek. They stay at campgrounds, and take turns cooking, cleaning up, planning menus and shopping for them. Usually they stay long enough to go fishing, backpacking, rafting, canoeing, rock climbing or exploring and have evening campfire songs, stories or an astronomy session. "Mark and Tom are devoted, sensitive, fair leaders and knowledgeable about birds and plants," a parent writes. "The supervision was excellent and the program thoughtful. Can't say enough good things about this trip." They camp mostly in national, state and provincial parks, forests and seashores—but they also see Montreal, New York, Washington, Williamsburg and Atlanta, plus museums, outdoor drama and a Broadway musical for variety. Trips vary each year; also week-long spring trips.

☐ New England/Canada tour, Jun. 15–Aug. 2, $985. *Mark Levin, Dir., Open Road Experiences, Country Day School, 300 Park Rd., Metairie, Louisiana 70005. Tel.: (504) 837-5204.*

Maine

CHEWONKI FOUNDATION provides meaningful and exciting programs for young people—and for entire families. For 14- to 17-year-olds there are 8-week wilderness outings for groups of ten boys and two leaders. One trip involves canoeing and backpacking in the Maine woods; another is for kayaking on the upper Androscoggin and the Rapid River; and a seamanship program takes boys along the Maine coast in wooden rowing and sailing boats. Also a 6-week Mistassini River trip in northern Quebec. For boys 9 to 12 and 13 to 15, there are 8-week summer camps on the foundation's 400 acre peninsula surrounded by tidal bays, inlets, mountains and rivers. This also is the setting for a 7-day family ecology workshop featuring nature study and also tennis, swimming, sailing and canoeing; and the starting point for family camping trips on the Allagash or St. Croix Rivers for 7 to 10 days. "Canoe camping is so different from car camping," Tim Ellis points out. "These river trips are confidence-builders for families that want to learn how to do it." A 2-week family boat building program, and a school, Maine Reach, for seniors or high school graduates, also are offered. Personal growth, community awareness and sensitivity to the natural world are goals in each of the non-profit organization's programs.

☐ Wilderness outings, late Jun. to mid-Aug.: 8 weeks, $1,300–$1,400; 6 weeks, $1,000. Mid-Aug. to Labor Day: 7-day ecology workshop, $120 for 1, $200 for 2, $65 each addl.; river camping trips, 7-10 days, $140–$200/person. Location: 45 mi. NE of Portland. *Tim Ellis, Director, Chewonki Foundation, Wiscasset, Maine 04578. Tel.: (207) 882-7323.*

Acadian Summer Camp, Louisiana

Minnesota

CIRCLE R RANCH, INC., with 100 riding horses, has you doing special things all year long. Summers are set aside for coed camping as 9- to 16-year-olds take over the riding and horse shows—all under excellent supervision. "This is a down-to-earth operation," writes a parent, "fairly simple, which we like. The food is excellent, as are the counselors. The Raabs have an excellent way with children. The week goes by too fast in this relaxed, home-like atmosphere." Trail rides, tennis, go-carts, hayrides, pony carts, swimming pool, overnight campouts and recreation room fun are just part of the goings-on. September to May it's for families and groups, who take cues from the weather and the season. In winter they're out there snowmobiling.

☐ Summer camp, $120/week, disct. for 2 or more weeks. Sep.–May, A $30/weekend, C under 8, $15. Rates incl. riding. 112 mi. NW of Minneapolis. From Little Falls go W on Rt. 27 for 15 mi., ranch on left. Meet plane/train/bus in Little Falls, no chg. *Dallas & Vivian Raab, Circle R Ranch, Inc., Rt. 1, Long Prairie, Minnesota 56347. Tel.: (612) 547-2176.*

Montana

SHINING MOUNTAIN RANCH, on 6,000 acres in western Montana, is a camp with separate areas for boys and girls. They experience an old-time mountain horse ranch as it might have been in the late 1800s. Each one has the use of "your own horse" chosen from the ranch's 150 head. Campers care for animals, help with ranch chores, build fence and sometimes help build a cabin. They also swim in a private lake, fish the trout streams, backpack and go on overnight horseback trips. Bill Mitchell believes in "the highest standards of safety, nutrition and staff capability." Parents comment that it's an "excellent camp, very well run, with a staff that is committed to the sound development of these youngsters." ACA accredited.

☐ Sessions late-Jun. to late-Aug. 4 weeks, $695–$995; 9 weeks, $1,550–$1,850. Rates vary for dates & programs chosen. Options: 5-day wilderness horseback trip, $165; 6-day vehicle tour, $225. Off US 93 S of Missoula. *W.L. Mitchell, Dir., Shining Mountain Ranch, Box 251-F, Sula, Montana 59871. Tel.: (406) 821-3729.*

Pennsylvania

LONGACRE FARM, owned by three young couples, plays host to about 30 teenagers every summer. The intensive rural ex-

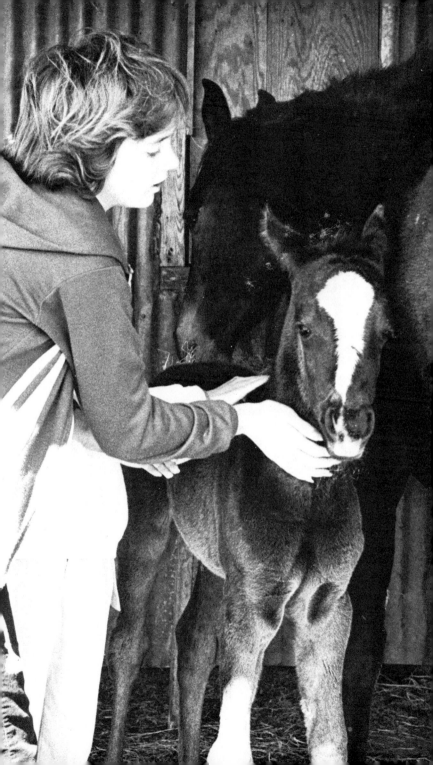

Longacre Farm, Pennsylvania

perience gives each a real taste of what it's like to be a farmer. "It's particularly well suited for bright, motivated teenagers who wish to expand their horizons," writes a parent; and a young guest call it "a fantastic experience." Participants learn directly about rural life by caring for the goats, pigs, chickens and cows; tending and harvesting the large garden; and plowing, planting, cultivating and reaping field crops. They sleep in platform tents, cook in the kitchen, visit auctions and dairy farms, go sailing and fishing and more. The Bornsteins, Houldins and Smiths combine their years as educators and camp counselors, and other professional skills, in the experience they offer teenagers. "They create an atmosphere of warmth, love and inspiration and are outstanding in their work with young people," a parent states.

☐ Jul. 1–Aug. 25, 6 weeks $940, 8 weeks $1,140. 100 mi. W of Philadelphia, 30 mi. NW of Harrisburg. *Longacre Farm, R.D. 3, Box 40, Newport, Pennsylvania 17074. Tel.: (717) 567-6790, 3795 or 3349.*

Texas

CAMP CHAPARRAL is a working ranch that becomes a Coed Ranch Camp from June through August where 7- to 14-year-olds can experience farm and ranch life with the friendly and knowledgeable Seifferts. Bugle call comes from the roosters, followed by breakfast at the chuck kitchen. Then it's saddle-up time, off on the trails, sometimes picknicking at lakeside or along a creek. Afternoons are filled with swimming, crafts, art, drama, tennis or just playing. Hayrides, campfires, storytelling, scavenger hunts—all sorts of fun—in the evenings. "We like to give all children, especially city children, the actual experience of living on a farm while teaching them the usual camp skills and crafts," explains "Aunt Bettie" Seiffert. (Families and groups welcome the rest of the year—see listing under "Texas.")

☐ Camp session, 4 wks., Jun. thru Aug., $660. 50 mi. S of San Antonio. Meet plane there, $10/carload, or bus in Pleasanton, no chg. *Ernest & Bettie Seiffert, Camp Chaparral, Box 30, Christine, Texas 78012. Tel.: (512) 784-3233.*

WEAVER RANCH is a special place for kids (8 to 14 years) who love animals and rodeos and the outdoors—who don't mind getting hot and dirty. "We don't fancy it up for them in any way," caution the Weavers. The ranch house becomes the young guests' home, and they learn the fundamentals of horsemanship, barrel racing, roping, pole bending and the like. The Weavers maintain a rodeo arena right on the ranch. "Our daughter really loves them," states a parent. "They gave her confidence in herself to do a lot of new things." The ranch has been in continuous operation under one family since 1874, and the Weavers want guests to feel it's "sort of like staying with Grandma and Grandpa on the farm, busy and fun." The kids also gather eggs, make ice cream, bottle feed a dogie calf, help check cattle and fences, go on roundups, overnight campouts and cookouts, catch fish and go swimming. (See also listing in "Texas" section.)

☐ Separate sessions for girls & boys 8–14 yrs. sched. Jun. thru Aug., Sun. p.m. to Sat. noon. $175/week. 80 mi. S of Dallas, 45 mi. E of Waco. *Ted & Shirley Weaver, Weaver Ranch, Rt. 1, Wortham, Texas 76693. Tel.: (817) 765-3489.*

Vermont

FARM & WILDERNESS CAMPS, six of them, are for boys, girls or both between 9 and 17 years. Emphasis varies from trail blazing, bird walks, campcraft and foraging at one, to rock climbing, backpacking and exploring at another. At Tamarack Farm, for example, coeds 15 to 17 milk the cow and goats, feed the animals, cultivate and harvest organic gardens, churn butter, cut hay and mend fences. At each camp there are many fun activities along with the productive program. Whatever the camp's individual characteristic, the Quaker values of simplicity, honesty, self-reliance and mutual respect are observed. The camps are non-denominational (about a quarter of the campers are Quakers), and are established on 3,000 beautiful acres of forest, lakes and meadows. A camper-staff ratio of four to one insures individual care and excellent supervision. ACA accredited.

☐ Camps in July & Aug., 4 weeks, $730, 8 weeks, $1,190. 140 mi. NW of Boston, 23 mi. E of Rutland. *Ridgway Satterthwaite, Exec. Director, Farm & Wilderness Camps, Plymouth, Vermont 05056. Tel.: (802) 422-3445.*

MERRY MEADOW FARM is a place to find well-trained horses and knowledgeable horsemanship instruction. The Williams family breed and train Thoroughbred and Morgan horses, and 10- to 16-year-olds come here for all levels of instruction. Based on U.S. Pony Club goals, each student cares for a horse and equipment. (Some bring their own.) Twice-daily riding in outside rings, 70- by 140-foot indoor arena or on trails is followed by a swim in the pool, hiking, canoeing or visiting the area. Each session ends with mounted games and a horse show, and one USCTA combined training event is held each summer. A limited number of students ensures maximum individual attention. Excellent meals are served family style in the big, sunny farm kitchen. Whatever the activity, these are capable and happy people to do it with, and their horses are interesting and challenging companions. (See "Vermont" section for family vacations at other times.)

☐ Bunkhouse & rooms in farmhouse for camp sessions, July thru mid-Aug. $350 for 2-week session (rates for addl. sessions). 150 mi. NW of Boston. Meet plane/train/bus in Lebanon, White River Jct., or Bradford. *Jack & Betty Williams, Merry Meadow Farm, Bradford, Vermont 05033. Tel.: (802) 222-4412.*

STUDENT HOSTELING PROGRAM trips "are not for everyone," Ted Lefkowitz emphasizes. "While the possibilities for fun and adventure are great, they are emotionally and physically demanding and require self-discipline and a reasonable level of maturity. Pot, drugs and alcoholic beverages are not allowed." For 13- to 17-year-olds who furnish their own 10-speed bikes, SHP offers 2- to 6-week non-tourist bicycling-hiking-camping trips in the U.S., Canada and Europe. Coed groups are small—no more than ten with two leaders. They travel by bicycle and on foot at their own pace using campsites, hostels and mountain huts, buy food at local markets and cook

Merry Meadow Farm, Vermont

their own meals. They average 25 to 40 miles on travel days and explore on layover days. "If I could stay young forever, I would return forever," reports a participant. The directors, Ted and Barbara, have led hosteling trips for 14 years. Their goal is to give teenagers a chance to learn about the world, the beauty of life and themselves through experiences of their own making. Trips begin in Boston and end at major airports.

☐ Trips Jun. thru Aug., w./insurance & equipment pkg., approx. $20–$25/day in U.S. & Canada, $40/day in Europe incl. air. *Ted & Barbara Lefkowitz, Student Hosteling Program, Box C, Maple Hill, Rochester, Vermont 05767. Tel.: (802) 767-3297.*

Washington

BAR 41 RANCH borders Lake Roosevelt, and the Longaneckers raise cattle, horses, fruit and hay on their 1,300 acres. But from mid-June 'til the end of August their attention centers on kids from 7 to 18 years old who come here for horsemanship classes, daily rides and all the other things that go with it—crafts, campouts, hikes, riflery, archery, hayrides, skits and songfests. And every afternoon they're at the beach—swimming, boating, and waterskiing. "A spirit of love shows in every activity," a parent reports. "It's well-supervised, with superb fellowship." Bettering human relations through camp experience is a goal at the camp, and everyone gives a helping hand to an occasional handicapped camper. The rest of the year the camp welcomes families and small group retreats.

☐ Camp sessions: 1 week, $140; 2 weeks, $260. Family or group visits, weekly AP: A $137, C $102; daily, A $20 & C $16; riding extra. *The Longanecker Family, Bar 41 Ranch, Star Rt., Wilbur, Washington 99185. Tel.: (509) 647-5487.*

Wyoming

VALLEY RANCH, a working guest ranch, gives young people from 10 to 15 a chance to become "Wilderness Riders" through the month of July. Each is given a horse to match riding ability, and is responsible for it during this time. Riders learn how to pack their horses and set up camp, skills which they use on a 10-day pack trip into the Washakie Wilderness Area. They participate in all the ranch activities—hayrides, cookouts, games, square dances and campfire sings—and celebrate the Fourth of July by going to the Cody Stampede Rodeo. Arts, crafts and photography are part of the program. (For family vacations, see listing in "Wyoming" section.)

☐ "Wilderness Riders" program, July, $1,075 plus slight crafts/photog. fee. *Oak & Lisa Thorne, Valley Ranch, South Fork Star Route V, Cody, Wyoming 82414. Tel.: (307) 587-4661.*

White Pines Ranch, Illinois

Appendix

This Appendix is added as an aid to locating a vacation spot that meets certain specific requirements.

Are you seeking a real, working farm or ranch? Or one where your children will be welcome whether or not you go with them? Perhaps you'd like to get away to a place geared only for adults, or where your rural hosts provide a cabin complete with facilities for cooking your own meals.

Property where they can camp or park a trailer satisfies some vacationers. Being where most guests do—or do not—smoke or drink is important to others. An airstrip either on the property or nearby, with pickup service, is a necessity for anyone arriving in a private plane.

An Addenda comments on jobs at farms and refers to Jewish Dietary Laws.

Information to guide your choice is included here. In each case, for a detailed description, please turn to the coverage of the farm, ranch, lodge or inn which appears on an earlier page of this book.

I Working Farms and Ranches

What's a "working" farm or ranch? Not one where you are *required* to feed the animals, milk the cows, round up cattle, mend fences, weed the garden or harvest crops—but one where you can help with these and other activities *if you wish* and learn a lot in the process. Best of all, you really get to know your hosts, since you're living and sharing as a guest in their home.

This differs from what we call a "guest" farm or ranch (or a "dude" ranch) in that only a few guests at a time are accommodated—perhaps one or two families or couples. And the "activities program" consists of whatever happens to be going on at the time.

If you prefer being where more is planned for guests—where you'll be joining maybe 15 or 20 (or 50+) other vacationers for fun events that may include a heated swimming pool, square dances, trail rides, gymkhanas, barbecues, a program for the kids and more—choose a place *not* mentioned here.

Arizona
  Price Canyon Ranch

California
  Cholame Creek Ranch

Colorado
  Canyon Ranch
  S Bar S Ranch
  Wilson's Pinto Bean Farm

Connecticut
  Constitution Oak Farm

Florida
  DeHaan Farm

Indiana
  Sycamore Spring Farm

Iowa
  Little House in the Woods

Kansas
  Thurlow Vacation Farm

Kentucky
  Brown's Vacation Farm
  Strathmere Farm
  Walnut Springs Farm

Maryland
  Mountain View Farm

Massachusetts
  Fiske Farm
  Rite-View Farm

Minnesota
  Honeysuckle Farm

Missouri
  Organic Acres

Montana
  Blacktail Ranch
  Canyon Ranch
  Halter Ranch
  Hell Creek Guest Ranch
  Hidden Hollow
  Leffingwell's G Bar M Ranch
  Rooney Ranches

Nebraska
  Pine Hills Ranch

Nevada
  Nixon Ranch

New York
  Far View Farm
  Glen Durham
  Holiday Acres
  Merrill's Farm

North Dakota
  Hansen Family Farm

Ohio
  Circle K Ranch
  Wallace's Wooded Acres
  Windy Acres

Oregon
  Green Springs Box R Ranch
  Hurtley Quarter Horse Ranch

Pennsylvania
  Dyberry Glen
  Gran Pino Farms
  Hillside Farms
  Hillstone Farms
  Landis Farm Guest Home
  Loujean Acres

Mayfield
Rosebrook Cottage
Swa-Nea Acres
Verdant View Farm
Water Co., The
Windmere Farm
Windmill Farm
Wyant Acres

South Dakota
Cross Ranch
Skoglund Farm

Texas
Camp Chaparral
Weaver Ranch

Utah
Navajo Cliffs Ranch

Vermont
Knoll Farm Country Inn

Merry Meadow Farm
Reevesdale Farm
Rodgers Dairy Farm

Virginia
Shenandoah Valley Farm

Wisconsin
Ethilton Farms
Happy Acres
Harmony Hill Farms
Hillview Vacation Home

Wyoming
Cross Milliron Ranch
Deer Forks Ranch
Diamond Seven Bar Ranch
Fir Creek Ranch
Pellatz Ranch
Whistle Creek Ranch
Zimmerschied Ranch

II Children Alone

The chapter "For Teens and Under" (page 191) tells of activities developed especially for young people. But many of the host families covered throughout this book are happy to have young people visit whether or not their parents come along. It's like staying with cousins, and pitching in with chores and other activities as a member of the family. The places listed here extend an invitation to young people alone—as well as to families and adults.

Arizona
Price Canyon Ranch

California
Cholame Creek Ranch

Colorado
Canyon Ranch
Sun Valley Guest Ranch
Wilson's Pinto Bean Farm

Illinois
Hobson's Bluffdale

Kansas
Thurlow Vacation Farm

Montana
Canyon Ranch
Circle Eight Ranch
Halter Ranch
Hidden Hollow
Sixty Three Ranch
Sweet Grass Ranch

New Hampshire

Pease's Scenic Valley

New York
Glen Durham
Golden Acres Farm Resort

North Dakota
Hansen Family Farm

Ohio
Circle K Ranch
McNutt Farm

Pennsylvania
Loujean Acres
Verdant View Farm

South Dakota
Cross Ranch
Skoglund Farm

Texas
Camp Chaparral
Weaver Ranch

Vermont
Merry Meadow Farm

Wisconsin
    Ethilton Farms
    Farm, The
    Hunky Dory Farms

Wyoming
    Castle Rock Ranch
    Diamond Seven Bar Ranch
    Valley Ranch
    Zimmerschied Ranch

III Adults Only

At most of the places we list, all through the book, vacationer ages range from toddlers to great-grandfathers, with activities that satisfy everyone. But sometimes adults want a vacation free from mingling with the younger set. These places are for them:

Massachusetts
    Maples, The

Michigan
    Double JJ Resort Ranch

New York
    Holiday Acres

Vermont
    Whitetail Corners Guest House

IV Housekeeping Units

Doing their own cooking (or going out for meals) is no chore for some vacationers, and they may prefer the extra privacy of staying in housekeeping facilities. This arrangement, depending upon your choice, can be easier on the budget than American Plan (with meals) rates. Some units large enough for the whole family are available at a minimum $75 to $100 a week. Others are much more. Frequently the farm produce is yours for the gathering, at a nominal cost or none at all.

The list below will help in spotting these places where European Plan (accommodations without meals) rates are offered on rooms, apartments, separate cabins, bunkhouses or an entire farmhouse large enough for a whole group.

Alaska
    Camp Denali

Arizona
    Kay El Bar Guest Ranch
    Loba Lodge
    Lomaqaci
    Sunglow Mission Ranch

Arkansas
    Rolling Acres Ranch

California
    Camanche North Shore Resort
    Rocking R Ranch

Colorado
    Arapaho Valley Ranch
    MacTiernan's San Juan Ranch
    S Bar S Ranch
    Vista Verde Guest Ranch

Wilson's Pinto Bean Farm

Connecticut
    Inn on Lake Waramaug

Florida
    De Haan Farm

Hawaii
    Kahili Mountain Park

Iowa
    Little House in the Woods

Kentucky
    Brown's Vacation Farm
    Whitney Longview Farm

Maine
    Edgewater Motel & Cottages
    Homewood Inn
    Kinapic Housekeeping Cottages

McGrath Pond Camps
Mohan Cottage
Oakland House
Town Line Campsites

Maryland
Glenarm Farm
Mountain View Farm

Massachusetts
Maples, The

Minnesota
Fair Hills Resort
Honeysuckle Farm

Missouri
Organic Acres

Montana
Canyon Ranch
Ford Creek Ranch

New Hampshire
Pease's Scenic Valley

New Mexico
Bear Mountain Guest Ranch

New York
Elms Farm Inn
Fieldstone Farm
Garnet Hill Lodge
Golden Acres Farm Resort
Hartelius Cottages
Little Texas Ranch
Merwin's Fishing Preserve, Inc.
Mountainbrook Chalet
Wheathill Holstein
Willow Side

North Carolina
Lullwater Inn
Springdale Lodge

Ohio
Circle K Ranch
McNutt Farm
Twin Valley Farm & Campground
Wallace's Wooded Acres

Windy Acres

Oregon
Donna Gill's Rock Springs Guest Ranch
Green Springs Box R Ranch
Hurtley Quarter Horse Ranch

Pennsylvania
Beaver Creek Farm Cabins
Hillstone Farms
Inn at Starlight Lake
Lake Mount Farm
Landis Farm Guest Home
Loujean Acres
Orchard Rock Cottages
Quality First Acres
Rosebrook Cottage
Windmill Farm
Wyant Acres

Texas
Whispering Winds

Vermont
Bell-Mott-Beach Cottages
Brook Bound Lodge & Chalets
Melis Farms

Virginia
Deer Tracks Lodge
Graves' Mountain Lodge
Montfair Family Resort & Farm
Shenandoah Valley Farm

Washington
Flying L Ranch

Wisconsin
Camp Lake Resort
Harmony Hill Farms
Hillview Vacation Home

Wyoming
Deer Forks Ranch
Diamond Seven Bar Ranch
Shoshone Lodge

Virgin Islands
Sprat Hall Plantation

V Bring Your Horse

Some people would rather stay home than go on vacation without their own horse. Listed here are places where both will be welcome.

Check with the hosts on details: Do they provide straight stalls, box stalls or fenced pasture? Will they furnish feed, hay and oats or should you bring these along? To what extent can you ride on their property or nearby? Rates vary from $1 per night up—for your horse, that is.

Arizona
  Kay El Bar Guest Ranch
  Loba Lodge
  Price Canyon Ranch
  Sunglow Mission Ranch

California
  Camanche North Shore Resort
  Cholame Creek Ranch
  Circle Bar B Guest Ranch
  Coffee Creek Ranch
  Flying H Western Guest Ranch
  Hunewill Circle H Guest Ranch
  Lor-O-Ranch
  M Bar J Guest Ranch
  Rocking R Ranch

Colorado
  Beavers Guest Ranch
  Canyon Ranch
  Indian Head Guest Ranch
  Lake Mancos Ranch
  MacTiernan's San Juan Ranch
  Snowshoe Guest Ranch
  Sun Valley Guest Ranch
  Trail's End Ranch
  Wilson's Pinto Bean Farm

Florida
  DeHaan Farm

Hawaii
  Kahili Mountain Park

Iowa
  Little House in the Woods

Kentucky
  Brown's Vacation Farm
  Strathmere Farm
  Whitney Longview Farm

Maryland
  Mountain View Farm

Massachusetts
  Foxhollow Resort

Montana
  Blacktail Ranch
  Circle Eight Ranch
  Flathead Lake Lodge
  Ford Creek Ranch
  Halter Ranch
  Hell Creek Guest Ranch
  Hidden Hollow
  Lone Mountain Ranch
  Nine Quarter Circle Ranch
  Rooney Ranches
  Sixty Three Ranch
  Sweet Grass Ranch

Nebraska
  Pine Hills Ranch

Nevada
  Nixon Ranch

New Hampshire
  Inn at East Hill Farm
  Pease's Scenic Valley

New Mexico
  Bear Mountain Guest Ranch

New York
  All Breeze Guest Farm
  Bogg's Riverside
  Far View Farm
  Fieldstone Farm
  Glen Durham
  Golden Acres Farm Resort
  Holiday Acres
  Little Texas Ranch
  Rocking Horse Ranch
  Roundup Ranch
  Willow Side

North Carolina
  Cataloochee Ranch
  Pisgah View Ranch

North Dakota
  Hansen Family Farm

Ohio
  McNutt Farm

Oregon
  Donna Gill's Rock Springs Guest Ranch
  Green Springs Box R Ranch
  Hurtley Quarter Horse Ranch

Pennsylvania
  Chestnut Hill Ranch
  Hillstone Farms
  Mayfield
  Posey Patch Acres
  Silver Lake House
  Water Co., The

South Dakota
  Cross Ranch
  Skoglund Farm

Texas
  Camp Chaparral
  Lazy Hills Guest Ranch
  Weaver Ranch

Utah
  Navajo Cliffs Ranch

Vermont
  Brook Bound Lodge & Chalets

Melis Farms
Merry Meadow Farm
Weathervane Lodge

Virginia
Graves' Mountain Lodge
Montfair Family Resort & Farm
Rounton Farm

Washington
Flying L Ranch

Wisconsin
Ethilton Farms
Harmony Hill Farms
Hunky Dory Farms

Wyoming
Bill Cody's Ranch Inn
Castle Rock Ranch
Deer Forks Ranch
Diamond Seven Bar Ranch
Goosewing Ranch
Hidden Valley Ranch
Lost Creek Ranch
Medicine Bow Lodge & Guest Ranch
Pellatz Ranch
Togwotee Mountain Lodge
Whistle Creek Ranch

Virgin Islands
Sprat Hall Plantation

VI Camping and Trailer Sites

This book is not a guide to campgrounds, but many of the rural hosts it lists are happy to have campers or RV people come by for a visit. Whereas most of them do not provide any special facilities, some have campsites equipped with water supply, sewage and garbage disposal, tentsite, picnic table, fireplace or grill, flush or dry toilet and access road. Some (or all) of these facilities are furnished at the places marked with an asterisk (*).

Similarly, those with electric outlets for trailers, water and sewage connections, showers, etc., are so marked.

Campsites

Alaska
Brooks Lodge

Arizona
Price Canyon Ranch*

Arkansas
Rolling Acres Ranch

California
Camanche North Shore Resort*
Lor-O-Ranch*

Florida
DeHaan Farm

Kentucky
Brown's Vacation Farm
Whitney Longview Farm

Maine
Mohan Cottage
Town Line Campsites*

Maryland
Mountain View Farm

Missouri
Organic Acres

Montana
Halter Ranch
Rooney Ranches

Nebraska
Pine Hills Ranch

Nevada
Nixon Ranch

New Hampshire
Pease's Scenic Valley

New York
All Breeze Guest Farm
Golden Acres Farm Resort*
Holiday Acres
Little Texas Ranch

North Carolina
Lullwater Inn*
Pisgah View Ranch*

Ohio
Twin Valley Farm & Campground*

Oregon
Hurtley Quarter Horse Ranch*

Pennsylvania
   Hillstone Farms*
   Loujean Acres
   Water Co., The

South Dakota
   Cross Ranch*
   Skoglund Farm*

Texas
   Camp Chaparral

Utah

   Navajo Cliffs Ranch

Virginia
   Montfair Family Resort & Farm*

Wisconsin
   Camp Lake Resort
   Ethilton Farms
   Vacationland Farm*

Wyoming
   Diamond Seven Bar Ranch
   Togwotee Mountain Lodge*

Trailer Sites

Arizona
   Price Canyon Ranch*

Arkansas
   Rolling Acres Ranch

California
   Camanche North Shore Resort
   Lor-O-Ranch*

Colorado
   Wilson's Pinto Bean Farm*

Florida
   DeHaan Farm*

Maine
   Mohan Cottage*
   Town Line Campsites*

Maryland
   Mountain View Farm

Montana
   Ford Creek Ranch*
   Halter Ranch
   Rooney Ranches*

Nevada
   Nixon Ranch

New York
   Boggs' Riverside
   Far View Farm
   Golden Acres Farm Resort*
   Holiday Acres
   Little Texas Ranch

North Carolina
   Lullwater Inn*
   Pisgah View Ranch*

North Dakota
   Hansen Family Farm

Ohio
   Twin Valley Farm & Campground*

Oregon
   Hurtley Quarter Horse Ranch*

Pennsylvania
   Hillside Farm
   Hillstone Farms
   Landis Farm Guest Home
   Loujean Acres*
   Windmere Farm

South Dakota
   Cross Ranch*
   Skoglund Farm*

Virginia
   Montfair Family Resort & Farm*

Wisconsin
   Ethilton Farms

Wyoming
   Deer Forks Ranch*
   Diamond Seven Bar Ranch
   Togwotee Mountain Lodge*
   Zimmerschied Ranch*

VII Non-Smokers and Non-Drinkers

Vacationers are increasingly interested in the "ground rules" concerning smoking and drinking, especially at a working farm or ranch where they'll be sharing limited living and dining quarters with the hosts and other guests.

The lists below will be helpful to those who do smoke and enjoy a drink now and then, as well as to those who prefer being where there's apt to be little or no smoking or drinking.

Hosts' rules in this respect are not rigid, but those who prefer having non-smoking and non-drinking guests are listed below.

Non-Smokers

Arizona
  Lomaqaci
  Sunglow Mission Ranch

Arkansas
  Rolling Acres Ranch

California
  M Bar J Guest Ranch

Colorado
  Double JK Ranch
  Sylvan Dale Guest Ranch
  Waunita Hot Springs Ranch
  Wilson's Pinto Bean Farm

Indiana
  Sycamore Spring Farm

Kentucky
  Walnut Springs Farm

Maine
  Kinapic Housekeeping Cottages

Minnesota
  Honeysuckle Farm

Nebraska
  Pine Hills Ranch

Nevada
  Nixon Ranch

New Hampshire
  Rockhouse Mountain Farm Inn

New York
  Far View Farm
  Glen Durham
  Timberlock

North Carolina
  Folkestone Lodge
  Lullwater Inn

Ohio
  McNutt Farm

Oregon
  Green Springs Box R Ranch

Pennsylvania
  Landis Farm Guest Home
  Mayfield
  Saw-Nea Acres
  Verdant View Farm
  Water Co., The
  Windmere Farm
  Wyant Acres

South Dakota
  Cross Ranch

Texas
  Camp Chaparral
  Lazy Hills Guest Ranch
  Weaver Ranch

Vermont
  Knoll Farm Country Inn

Virginia
  Graves' Mountain Lodge

Washington
  Partridge Inn

Wyoming
  Diamond Seven Bar Ranch
  Fir Creek Ranch
  Pellatz Ranch

Non-Drinkers

Arizona
  Lomaqaci

Arkansas
  Rolling Acres Ranch

Colorado
  Double JK Ranch
  Lost Valley Ranch
  Sylvan Dale Guest Ranch
  Waunita Hot Springs Ranch

Indiana
  Sycamore Springs Farm

Kentucky
  Brown's Vacation Farm
  Walnut Springs Farm

Maine
  Kinapic Housekeeping Cottages

Maryland
  Mountain View Farm

Massachusetts
  Rite-View Farm

Minnesota
  Honeysuckle Farm

Montana
  Hidden Hollow
  Rooney Ranches

Nebraska
  Pine Hills Ranch

Nevada
  Nixon Ranch

New Hampshire
  Pease's Scenic Valley

New York
  Far View Farm
  Glen Durham
  Holiday Acres

North Carolina
  Folkestone Lodge
  Lullwater Inn
  Pisgah View Ranch

Ohio
  McNutt Farm
  Twin Valley Farm & Campground
  Windy Acres

Oregon
  Green Springs Box R Ranch

Pennsylvania
  Hillside Farm
  Landis Farm Guest Home
  Mayfield
  Orchard Rock Cottages
  Rosebrook Cottage
  Verdant View Farm
  Water Co., The
  Wyant Acres

South Dakota
  Cross Ranch

Texas
  Camp Chaparral
  Lazy Hills Guest Ranch
  Weaver Ranch

Vermont
  Knoll Farm Country Inn

Virginia
  Graves' Mountain Lodge

Washington
  Partridge Inn

Wisconsin
  Ethilton Farms
  Hunky Dory Farms

Wyoming
  Diamond Seven Bar Ranch
  Fir Creek Ranch
  Pellatz Ranch

VIII Airstrips

Airstrips throughout rural areas open up new vacation possibilities for private plane owners who like taking off for a weekend or longer.

We have asked each host listed in the book how close they are to an airport or landing strip for private planes. With some exceptions, the distance is from one to twenty or so miles, and they'll be glad to meet fly-ins for a small charge or none at all.

Several hosts have airstrips right on their own property:

Alaska
  Kulik Lodge

California
  Camanche North Shore Resort

Montana

Nine Quarter Circle Ranch

Vermont
  Merry Meadow Farm

Washington
  Flying L Ranch

IX Foreign Language

If you are visiting America and would like to vacation where someone can talk your native tongue, the list below will prove helpful. It refers to the places, state by state, where various languages are spoken.

"Speaking" your language can represent different stages of fluency, but someone in the host family or on the staff can bridge the language gap at least part way. And during the visit perhaps you'll improve your host's French or Spanish or German while you pick up a New England accent or a Texas drawl.

CZECHOSLOVAKIAN
Vermont
  Bell-Mott-Beach Cottages

DANISH
Virginia
  Rounton Farm
Wisconsin
  Hunky Dory Farms

DUTCH
California
  Coffee Creek Ranch
New York
  Golden Acres Farm Resort

FINNISH
Wisconsin
  Farm, The

FRENCH
Arizona
  Lomaqaci
California
  Circle Bar B Guest Ranch
  Quarter Circle U Rankin Ranch
Colorado
  Canyon Ranch
Connecticut
  Inn on Lake Waramaug
Kentucky
  Strathmere Farm
Maine
  Kinapic Housekeeping Cottages
Massachusetts
  Maples, The
Montana
  Flathead Lake Lodge
  Leffingwell's G Bar M Ranch
  Nine Quarter Circle Ranch
New Hampshire
  Rockhouse Mountain Farm Inn
  Snowvillage Lodge
New Mexico
  Los Pinos Ranch
New York
  Golden Acres Farm Resort
North Carolina
  Cataloochee Ranch
Pennsylvania
  Dyberry Glen
  Hillstone Farms

  Mayfield
  Orchard Rock Cottages
Vermont
  Bell-Mott-Beach Cottages
  Knoll Farm Country Inn
  Rodgers Dairy Farm
  Whitetail Corners Guest House
Virginia
  Rounton Farm
Wyoming
  Castle Rock Ranch
  Hidden Valley Ranch
  Whistle Creek Ranch

GERMAN
Arizona
  Lomaqaci
California
  Camanche North Shore Resort
Colorado
  Canyon Ranch
  Peaceful Valley Lodge
Montana
  Flathead Lake Lodge
New Hampshire
  Rockhouse Mountain Farm Inn
New York
  Fieldstone Farm
  Golden Acres Farm Resort
  Mountainbrook Chalet
  Polster's Farm Resort
South Dakota
  Cross Ranch
Vermont
  Knoll Farm Country Inn
Virginia
  Rounton Farm
Washington
  Flying L Ranch
Wisconsin
  Harmony Hill Farms

HUNGARIAN
Pennsylvania
  Dyberry Glen

ITALIAN
Colorado
  MacTiernan's San Juan Ranch
Nevada
  Nixon Ranch
Pennyslvania

Inn at Starlight Lake
Orchard Rock Cottages

LITHUANIAN
New Hampshire
Pease's Scenic Valley

NORWEGIAN
Virginia
Rounton Farm

Wisconsin
Hillview Vacation Home

POLISH
Pennsylvania
Windmill Farm

PORTUGUESE
Pennsylvania
Verdant View Farm

SPANISH
Arizona
Loba Lodge
Price Canyon Ranch
California
Circle Bar B Guest Ranch
Hunewill Circle H Guest Ranch
Quarter Circle U Rankin Ranch
Colorado
MacTiernan's San Juan Ranch
Sylvan Dale Guest Ranch
Massachusetts
Maples, The
Montana
Flathead Lake Lodge
Leffingwell's G Bar M Ranch
Sweet Grass Ranch

Nevada
Nixon Ranch
New Hampshire
Pease's Scenic Valley
Snowvillage Lodge
New Mexico
Los Pinos Ranch
New York
Fieldstone Farm
Garnet Hill Lodge
North Carolina
Folkestone Lodge
Oregon
Donna Gill's Rock Springs Guest Ranch
Pennsylvania
Orchard Rock Cottages
Verdant View Farm
South Dakota
Skoglund Farm
Texas
Lazy Hills Guest Ranch
Virginia
Montfair Family Resort & Farm
Wyoming
7-D Ranch
Virgin Islands
Sprat Hall Plantation

SWEDISH
Montana
Blacktail Ranch
South Dakota
Skoglund Farm
Virginia
Rounton Farm
Wisconsin
Vacationland Farm

X Addenda

To answer queries about getting jobs on farms and ranches, may we suggest contacting the hosts directly, since we do not gather this information. Perhaps you could arrange a pre-season trip to make your abilities known and to interview neighboring farmers or ranchers who may need some extra help.

For those inquiring about Jewish Dietary Laws, they are observed at a farm resort listed on page 108–109.

Index

FARM, RANCH & COUNTRY VACATIONS by Pat Dickerman is now scheduled for annual publication. Please use the self-mailer (next page) to request price and publication date for the 1980 edition . . . or to order copies of this 1979 book.

ADVENTURE TRAVEL by Pat Dickerman gives vacationers an insight into all kinds of adventurous treks. It puts them directly in touch with the experts who teach them how to do it and guide them, whether experienced or not, on wilderness excursions throughout North America.

Written for people of all ages who want a different and rewarding vacation with challenge, action, learning and fun, each of the 26 chapters covers in depth one activity: backpacking, rafting trips, mountaineering, pack trips by horse, walking trips with packstock carrying the gear, biking, jeeping, covered wagon trips, boat charters, windjammers, canoeing and kayaking, scuba diving, dog sledding, ski touring, snowmobiling, ballooning, parachuting, soaring, wilderness living, excursions especially for teens, and more.

Details include descriptions of trips, how many trekkers can join various guided excursions, whether outfitters can arrange custom trips for a family or group, what equipment they provide, and their rates, names, addresses and telephone numbers for making reservations. This is the 1978 (fourth) edition, with the next one scheduled for 1980.

For anyone with an adventurous and inquisitive spirit, the book provides a wealth of specific vacation ideas.

Both books are also available at many book stores.

For your comments:

1979 PRICES (including shipping charge):

   1 book, $6.50; 2nd book, $6.25; each additional book in same order, $6.00.

Please send me the following books by Pat Dickerman:

   ____ copy(ies) of *Farm, Ranch & Country Vacations* $_____

   ____ copy(ies) of *Adventure Travel (North America)*   _____

For delivery in New York City *add* 48¢ tax for each book.
For delivery in New York State *add* 24¢ tax for each book. . . . N.Y.C. or N.Y.S. tax _____

For delivery in Canada or Mexico *add* $1 for each book.
For delivery to other parts of the world *add* $3 for each book. . . Outside the U.S.A. _____

                        Check is enclosed for total $_____

       PAYMENTS FOR ORDERS OUTSIDE THE UNITED STATES:
       Please send full amount by U.S. or International Postal Money
       Order, or by a check in U.S. funds drawn on a U.S. bank.

☐ Please let me know when your 1980 editions will be ready, and the price.

Send books to: _____

                    _____

                    _____

       (We recommend inserting this self-mailer in an envelope if
       you are enclosing a check . . . or else staple it in securely.)

Seal

------------------------------ Fold ------------------------------

Farm & Ranch Vacations, Inc.
36 EAST 57th STREET
NEW YORK, N.Y. 10022

------------------------------ Fold ------------------------------

Seal